Overview of Artificial Intelligence Sciences and Technologies and their Contribution to an Intelligent Morocco

ScienciaScripts

Imprint

Any brand names and product names mentioned in this book are subject to trademark, brand or patent protection and are trademarks or registered trademarks of their respective holders. The use of brand names, product names, common names, trade names, product descriptions etc. even without a particular marking in this work is in no way to be construed to mean that such names may be regarded as unrestricted in respect of trademark and brand protection legislation and could thus be used by anyone.

Cover image: www.ingimage.com

This book is a translation from the original published under ISBN 978-620-3-45517-5.

Publisher:
Sciencia Scripts
is a trademark of
Dodo Books Indian Ocean Ltd. and OmniScriptum S.R.L publishing group

120 High Road, East Finchley, London, N2 9ED, United Kingdom
Str. Armeneasca 28/1, office 1, Chisinau MD-2012, Republic of Moldova, Europe

ISBN: 978-620-7-00935-0

Nourddin SAIDOU
Hssain TERJAOUI

Overview of Artificial Intelligence Sciences and Technologies and their Contribution to an Intelligent Morocco

Overview of Artificial Intelligence Sciences and Technologies and their Contribution to an Intelligent Morocco

Nourddin SAIDOU: Euromed University
Hssain TERJAOUI: ISTIGOP

Man and his safety must be the primary concern of any technological adventure". Albert Einstein

Agenda

Foreword

I) Introduction and background
II) General considerations on science, scientific and technological research and innovation for security and development in an era of global digital interdependence
  a) Overview
  b) International law of scientific and technical research, and international cooperation in the fields of science, scientific and technological research and innovation
  c) The digital revolution and its impact on the economy: transforming lifestyles, working methods, economic development and new technologies.

d) Links between the digital revolution and development
e) The rise of Artificial Intelligence (AI) technologies
f) Combining Artificial Intelligence technologies with other new technologies
g) Contribution of Artificial Intelligence to scientific discovery: exploring the potential of AI to accelerate the scientific discovery process and extract useful information from increasingly large datasets.
h) International cooperation at global and regional levels in the service of inclusive and trustworthy Artificial Intelligence, universal debate led on AI and international meetings dedicated to AI
i) Governance of Artificial Intelligence and organization of a Global Partnership on AI
j) Robotic technologies, drones, AI-powered autonomous vehicles and the emergence of AI-powered virtual idols in the cultural sphere
k) Artificial Intelligence, the Internet of Things and Industry 4.0
l) Artificial intelligence and cloud computing
m) Combining Artificial Intelligence and fifth-generation mobile telephony (5G)
n) Quantum Computing and Artificial Intelligence
o) Security issues, Artificial Intelligence against terrorism, security through science and the links between security and development
p) The complex links between safety and the environment
q) Artificial Intelligence technologies to solve ecological crises and water insecurity
r) Applications of Artificial Intelligence and robotics in the fabric of city life, airports, ports, railway stations and intelligent bus shelters
s) Intelligent security using Artificial Intelligence and robotics to facilitate public services in the fields of security and surveillance of illegal activities
t) Artificial Intelligence-powered spacecraft for safety and sustainable development with a human face
u) Contribution of Artificial Intelligence and robotics technologies to the fight against the new coronavirus pandemic (Covid-19)
v) Potential threats posed by Artificial Intelligence and questions about its misuse

w) Artificial intelligence and intellectual property

x) Trust in the reliability of Artificial Intelligence systems, and the ethics of AI and robotics: arguments in favor of responsible innovation, particularly in the field of AI research for the ethical use of algorithms in compliance with the principles of transparency, inclusion, accountability, impartiality, reliability and safety, and draft of the first global standard-setting instrument on the ethics of artificial intelligence, following the decision of UNESCO's General Conference at its 40ème session in November 2019

y) International standardization in the field of Artificial Intelligence

z) Summary and general conclusions and recommendations: Artificial Intelligence that is responsible, trustworthy, beneficial and promotes human values for high-quality, sustainable, inclusive, intelligent and resilient development.

III) Scientific and technological research in Artificial Intelligence and robotics, and use of AI and robotics technologies in the Kingdom of Morocco

a) Digital illiteracy and the existence of the "*technology left behind*" at a time of accelerated technological change and the dawn of the next technological revolution

b) Training in Artificial Intelligence and Robotics

c) Scientific and technological research in Artificial Intelligence and robotics in Morocco

d) Scientific and technological cooperation in Artificial Intelligence with foreign partners, particularly in Europe and China

e) Overview of the use of Artificial Intelligence and robotic technologies

f) Practical use of Artificial Intelligence and robotics applications in the national public security system

g) Summary, conclusions and general recommendations for tackling the diverse challenges posed by the range of insecurity situations and sustainable development through Artificial Intelligence and robotics

IV) Implementation of recommendations deserving immediate attention to the Kingdom of Morocco to ensure its intelligent national security for shared prosperity, including comprehensive human security in daily life, strengthen its political stability and promote high-quality, sustainable, inclusive, intelligent and resilient development.

a) The need to adapt the education and training system to provide the skills required for the digital economy, including skilled workers with the adaptability and creativity needed to "*work with machines*" and develop a thriving economy based on digital transformation and the knowledge economy.

b) Intelligent use of new technologies

c) Creating an environment conducive to unleashing the prodigious potential of Artificial Intelligence technologies to enhance overall national security and improve citizens' living conditions, by stepping up investment in science, technology, engineering and mathematics education, key drivers of the AI development ecosystem.

d) Intensify efforts to train the cutting-edge Artificial Intelligence talent Morocco needs to take advantage of the AI revolution, and stimulate the creation of highly dynamic startups developing AI-related uses.

e) Promoting scientific and technological research into Artificial Intelligence and robotics, particularly basic research, to stimulate innovation in AI that is trustworthy, ahead of technological developments and respectful of fundamental rights and ethical rules, making the most of the opportunities offered by AI and robotics, and meeting the challenges they pose and the challenges facing the Kingdom of Morocco: considerable national security issues.

f) Strengthening and diversifying sources of funding and direct investment for science, artificial intelligence and robotic technologies, and innovations that strengthen national security and facilitate the achievement of sustainable development goals for human progress.

g) Promoting the use of Artificial Intelligence and robotic technologies in all aspects of national security, the ecological crisis and the promotion of high-quality, sustainable, inclusive, intelligent and resilient development, and shared prosperity.

h) The need to put the transformative power of Artificial Intelligence at the service of Moroccan citizens, organizations and the economy for a better, more prosperous future for all, a future that ensures human control, trust, security, stability, the promotion of economic opportunities and environmental sustainability.

i) Promotion of Artificial Intelligence, a disruptive solution for monitoring and exploiting information to effectively and efficiently improve the Kingdom of Morocco's economic security, a cardinal component of the nation's security, ensuring that the economic crisis does not become a security crisis.

j) Using Artificial Intelligence to combat tax evasion and avoidance and enhance the sustainability of public finances and financial stability

k) Artificial Intelligence, the linchpin of Business Intelligence for the Kingdom of Morocco

l) Widespread adoption of explainable, transparent and responsible Artificial Intelligence in all sectors of the Moroccan economy

m) Applications of Artificial Intelligence in the field of public health safety (risk assessment, etc.), a strategic component of the nation's security, at the service, among other things, of emergency situations, to advance health for the good of all: offering a myriad of tools thanks to digital and Artificial Intelligence technologies.

n) Artificial intelligence for smart cities and regional planning, with a view to job creation, economic prosperity and high-quality, sustainable, inclusive, intelligent and resilient development.

o) Artificial Intelligence revolution to help prevent and manage natural disasters

p) Artificial intelligence, a future challenge for public services, in particular to combat the factors and impacts of insecurity situations

q) Artificial Intelligence, a guarantee of better living for citizens

r) Artificial intelligence for national defense and homeland protection

s) The need to guarantee a high level of cybersecurity

t) The importance of Artificial Intelligence for national sovereignty

u) Using the National Population Register and the Single Social Register in AI applications for security and development

v) True impacts of Artificial Intelligence on human society, the economy and public institutions, including the real potential impacts (socio-economic, cultural, human...) of intelligent national security using AI and robotics for a better and more sustainable future for all

w) The need to ensure an appropriate ethical and legal framework **for** Artificial Intelligence and robotics research to secure a better future and foster shared prosperity

x) Now is the time to take action to promote the Artificial Intelligence and Robotics ecosystem in order to, among other things, promote intelligent national security for shared prosperity, including comprehensive human security in everyday life, strengthen stability and promote the Kingdom of Morocco's high-quality, sustainable, inclusive, intelligent and resilient development.

V) Project for the structure responsible for carrying out the strategic multidisciplinary scientific research project

a) Given that Artificial Intelligence has become a strategic tool for many countries around the world, and that it is a technology of the future, involving the Kingdom of Morocco's economic interests, national security and national technological sovereignty in the field of Artificial Intelligence, it is necessary to set up a state structure responsible for carrying out the aforementioned strategic project.

h) to create this structure, given the crucial importance of its missions requiring the use of strategic and confidential information in Artificial Intelligence algorithms, at Her Majesty's or at the Ministry in charge of National Defense Administration,

ii) to name this structure Centre/Institut national de recherches pluridisciplinaires en Intelligence Artificielle et robotique or Centre/Institut Royal de recherches pluridisciplinaires en Intelligence Artificielle et robotique, a center of excellence promoting innovative AI in the service of intelligent homeland security, responsible and human-centered, in line with human rights, fundamental freedoms and shared democratic values.

Foreword

Technological advances are taking place at an unprecedented pace. Every day, new innovations appear thanks to the work of researchers and engineers. It's clear that they can do even better, for the benefit of institutions, citizens and businesses alike. Our technological prowess is impressive. Digital innovations play a crucial role in sectors such as healthcare, education and e-government,

In recent years, the world has witnessed the rise of Artificial Intelligence. We're seeing a growing volume of new articles, books and videos highlighting the revolution driven by Artificial Intelligence (AI). Today's technological mutations, in particular advances in Artificial Intelligence and massive data exploitation, are bringing about upheavals that are far beyond anything seen in the past. Artificial Intelligence technologies encompass machine learning, which in turn encompasses deep learning; they may also encompass several other types of software bricks. Artificial Intelligence in all its forms is set to revolutionize the human economy and society. All sectors are directly or indirectly concerned. Artificial Intelligence is the engine of the next industrial revolution. It's a business that the digital giants intend to corner.

Research into Artificial Intelligence (AI) and robotics is increasingly a multi-disciplinary undertaking, changing the way scientists work together. Scientific research in fundamental and applied AI is not a solitary endeavor. It takes place over the long term, with a wide range of seasoned profiles.

Conducting scientific research on, among other things, the development of mathematical models and algorithms, first at universities in Canada and then in Morocco, to the emergence, at national level, of issues linked to Artificial Intelligence and robotic technologies, we contacted high-level academics and scientific researchers from diverse scientific backgrounds, for whom AI has become a major focus of interest. The people contacted responded positively, expressing their enthusiasm for contributing to scientific research in AI in the service of high-quality development in the Kingdom of Morocco. In this way, a group of researchers from different horizons of knowledge and training, living in Morocco and abroad, is demonstrating synergy.

The present multidisciplinary scientific research work takes an integrated approach. It ardently aims at a common goal: serving the homeland, in particular, by providing stronger oversight of overall national security. The proposed multidisciplinary scientific research project offers an excellent level of stability for the Kingdom of Morocco, strengthening the capacity to protect the security of citizens and their property, to ensure the well-being of people, to guarantee the continuity of national life in all circumstances, to better rebuild the post-Covid-19 era and to promote high-quality, sustainable, inclusive and resilient development.

Artificial Intelligence (AI) and robotics are on a roll. Artificial Intelligence is brimming with possibilities. It's more than just a disruptive technology that will revolutionize the economy and human society. It's also a highly promising market. The development of AI technologies is part of the wider ecosystem of the Internet and other advanced ICTs, including megadata, the Internet of Things, blockchain and more. Artificial Intelligence, boosted by machine learning, is currently emerging as a revolution comparable to the Internet. Today, human life is increasingly governed by the diversity of technical applications associated with AI. In the field of Artificial Intelligence, the solutions developed are improving the management of public services and providing operational solutions to problems in promising sectors such as energy, the industry of the future and education. Increasingly, Artificial Intelligence is behind decision-making. Among other things, it will transform the way we produce, sell and even recruit. It will play a decisive role in the digital transformation of businesses. Although most autonomous software is designed to complement human skills, it will revolutionize many professions, just as machine tools did during the industrial revolution. Artificial Intelligence is a tool, albeit a highly sophisticated one, which is constantly evolving and improving as human intelligence deepens. Artificial Intelligence and robotic technologies occupy a growing place in our lives, and raise serious concerns about their responsible and ethical development.

The strategic project of multi-disciplinary scientific research deals with a wide range of issues linked to the development of AI. A group of researchers is essential to pool their multi-disciplinary capacities for analysis, anticipation and coordination in the field of AI.

As defined by the National Institute of Standards and Technology (NIST), cyber-physical systems (CPS) refer to "intelligent" co-constructed interactive networks of physical and computer components. As such, computer components and physical parts are tightly integrated. These cyber-physical systems range from small devices, such as implantable medical devices, to large-scale systems such as smart grids, nuclear power plants, water supply, healthcare systems, industrial control systems, financial systems, Industry 4.0 and smart buildings and smart cities.

In recent years, SPCs have emerged from traditional engineering systems in many fields such as energy, automotive and transportation, aerospace, buildings and healthcare. By massively deploying ubiquitous information and communication technologies in these systems, they have become smarter by providing a plethora of previously unsupported services (e.g. intelligent control, two-way communication, two-way energy flow, real-time sensing), in addition to improved responsiveness and efficiency. However, the deployment of information and communication technologies introduces new attack surfaces and new vulnerabilities for many of these mission-critical CPS, such as the intelligent network, where system availability and smooth operation are essential, even in the presence of failures. Exploitation of the above vulnerabilities will have dramatic consequences for security, privacy and safety.

As edge devices - hardware elements that control the flow of data at the boundary between two networks - become more powerful, miniaturized and inexpensive, it's possible to bring Artificial Intelligence, machine learning and real-time decision-making closer to where the data is produced. This means building privacy-friendly geo-distributed models and adapting decision-making algorithms to context. State-of-the-art IT systems will form the basis of CPS's smooth operation, particularly in time-sensitive tasks where even milliseconds count, such as remote robotic surgery or autonomous cars. They provide the necessary real-time information for these systems to operate and adapt in real time.

While the possibilities of CPS are seemingly endless, industry and decision-makers will need to focus on the dual agenda of delivering transformational products and services, while ensuring that they take into account the ethical and security ramifications. The creation of the proposed program is motivated by: (i) the imperative to secure the aforementioned cyber-physical systems against newly associated security threats; (ii) the vital obligation for Governments and businesses to protect cyber-physical systems against attacks that could result in serious economic and security consequences, or even endanger and kill. These attacks could be carried out by a wide range of individuals such as criminals, cyber-terrorists, terrorists and foreign government agencies; (iii) the availability of the body of knowledge in cyber-physical systems, and the essential need to study the security aspects arising from the intricate relationship between the computer and physical components of these systems; (iv) the creation of Artificial Intelligence technologies and systems that work well when integrated into human workflows with a practical impact on the world; (v) the urgent need to train highly qualified personnel to administer and operate the security of cyber-physical systems.

Demand for jobs in this field is growing and far outstripping supply, particularly in view of the changing threat landscape, the growing trend in cyber and physical incidents, the geopolitical context and the overriding importance of CPS system security. In fact, we're still at the dawn of cyber-physical systems and the IoT (Internet of Things); CPS and Artificial Intelligence technologies will increasingly be designed, deployed and integrated across a wide range of industrial sectors (e.g. aerospace, automotive, energy, transportation, healthcare, and defense). As a result, the strong demand for jobs will be both growing and sustainable.

Introduction and background

Science is the driving force behind innovation and development. Science, technology and innovation play a vital role and make a crucial contribution to helping countries become and remain competitive in the global economy, tackle global problems and achieve sustainable development,

Technological advances have long since revolutionized the world of work, among other things. Science and technology are the most powerful weapon in the battle for sustainable, inclusive, resilient and climate-friendly development. Digital technologies are now an integral part of people's daily lives. They are an inseparable part of any communications strategy, and highly effective in reaching diverse audiences. The innovations stimulated by digital technologies represent a potential for economic growth and driving social improvements in areas such as public administration, health, education and scientific research. Today, digital technology is also reflected in the use of Artificial Intelligence (AI). This encompasses a range of complex and powerful technologies that are affecting - indeed, transforming - all sectors and industries, and helping human society to solve many of its most challenging problems. The progress of AI is currently giving rise to fears of robots taking over, including highly-skilled jobs.

Artificial Intelligence technologies play an important role in the fight against epidemics, among other things. Epidemics know no borders or nations, and are a common enemy of humankind. Artificial Intelligence technologies are used to, among other things, design and develop vaccines and effective treatment against virus-caused diseases that require an imperative and united international response.

Science and technology are the most powerful weapons in mankind's battle against disease, including the current coronavirus pneumonia

(Covid-19) pandemic, which is spreading dangerously around the world, spreading human suffering and disrupting the global economy. The economic impact of the Covid-19 crisis is likely to claim even more victims than the virus itself.

A few days before the end of his term, French President François Hollande formulated, on March 21, 2017, in the Élysée Twitter account: "*The nations that master Artificial Intelligence will be the powers of tomorrow*". Furthermore, a few months later, during his university commencement speech, Russian President Vladimir Putin declared, on September 1er 2017, in front of Russian schoolchildren:
"Artificial Intelligence is the future, not just for Russia, but for all humanity. It presents colossal opportunities, but also threats that are difficult to foresee today. Whoever becomes the leader in this field will become the leader of the world".

Artificial Intelligence (AI) has become a field of strategic importance and a key driver of economic development. It can provide solutions to many societal challenges, from treating disease to reducing the environmental impact of agriculture. However, the socio-economic, legal and ethical impacts must be carefully considered.

Our research project has chosen to give priority to global and intelligent national security. It is committed, with ambition and responsibility, to the service of global human security and the development of the Kingdom of Morocco, in full coherence with the High Directions of His Majesty King Mohammed VI, may God assist Him. This report is divided into four parts:

II General considerations on science, scientific and technological research and innovation for security and development in an era of global digital interdependence;

III Scientific and technological research in AI and robotics, and use of AI and robotics technologies in the Kingdom of Morocco ;

IV Implementation of recommendations deserving immediate attention in the Kingdom of Morocco: the imperative need to promote scientific research and innovation, to use AI and robotic technologies, and to promote their ecosystem, in stages, in the field of national security, in order to promote sustainable and inclusive growth and development, aimed at leaving no one behind, in a prosperous Kingdom for all;

V Project for the structure responsible for carrying out our strategic multidisciplinary scientific research project.

II) General considerations on science, scientific and technological research and innovation for security and development in an era of global digital interdependence

a) Overview

Gone are the days when science was the work of inspired individuals who developed theories or designed experiments that could be carried out on a simple table and completed in a few days or weeks. Today, science often involves very large international teams whose work spans several years, or even decades. However, the time it takes for a scientific breakthrough to find applications is getting shorter, to the point where science and technology can change the world and make it unrecognizable in the space of a single generation. Today's world has come a long way thanks to science. Science has made life more comfortable than it was a century ago, but it has also made life more complicated. Humanity as a whole has applied the knowledge generated by science to the service of good. Science makes humanity progress. It has an ever-increasing influence on people's lives. It should be noted that indigenous knowledge contributes to the advancement of science.

Scientific discoveries have always begun with a hypothesis suggested by the imagination and a spirit of adventure. After imagination comes testing. Science and research are fundamental to mission accomplishment in all fields. Technological progress frees up work for new tasks and activities. Fundamental science is at the root of the technologies on which the information society is based. Progress comes in stages. Scientific expertise helps us to make important decisions in areas such as standards, regulations and policies.

In the global socio-economic battle, scientific research is increasingly serving the market and focusing on technological innovation. Science is increasingly seen as a "*commercial resource*". Major scientific and technological developments have taken place in many fields in recent years. The increasing use of robots in developed countries is eroding the traditional labor cost advantage of developing countries. Science, technology and globalization are transforming today's world, changing lives and shaping tomorrow's world. New information technologies are reducing distances and bringing people closer together. Science is behind the digital revolution. This revolution is still in progress. New technologies are destined to revolutionize every area of people's lives, shattering all previously solid walls one by one. Thanks to the digital revolution, calculation and measurement capacities will increase tenfold, and with them the ability to model phenomena whose complexity still eludes scientists. More than ever, mathematics will be the driving force behind scientific progress.

Rapid advances in digital technologies, driven by advances in computing, transmission speed and storage capacity, are transforming every aspect of human life. Building on the achievements of Artificial Intelligence, digital technologies are catalyzing breakthroughs in healthcare, the workplace and the economy. Together with advances in automation, robotics, nanotechnologies and biotechnologies, they are driving an unprecedented transformation of human interactions. Digital technologies can enable advances in areas such as the consolidation of national security.

While digital technologies have the potential to bring immense progress, they also run the risk of having negative repercussions on employment, livelihoods, privacy and personal security, facilitating the spread of hate speech and accentuating the polarization of opinions. Human interactions with devices and systems, as well as those of a social nature, are increasingly managed by Artificial Intelligence. This implies strong requirements to guarantee the security of critical AI applications, for example in healthcare systems, transportation, security and confidentiality of communication channels. Techniques and regulations need to be developed for the validation, certification and auditing of AI-related tools, to guarantee the trust they inspire.

Science, technology and innovation have both bright and dark sides. Despite the threats of nuclear apocalypse it has made possible, science is adorned with a beneficial aura. In East and West, North and South, it is invested with a sacred mission: to guarantee the prosperity and security of nations. Scientific progress benefits tomorrow's wars. Artificial Intelligence technologies are also used in theaters of war, either as a weapon of destruction (killer drones, etc.) or as a management tool for humanitarian missions: sending medicines, detecting safer routes for humanitarian aid, coordinating international responses, and so on. The definition of autonomous weapons systems is the subject of ongoing international debate. The term "autonomous weapon system" generally refers to weapon systems with a certain degree of autonomy for critical functions relating to offensive actions, such as target selection and firing. Lethal autonomous weapons, machines capable of killing beyond human control or responsibility, are taking communities into unacceptable moral and political territory. We are moving towards a world of killing machines beyond human discernment or control. Autonomous lethal weapons systems threaten to become the 3ème revolution in warfare. Russian President Putin declared in September 2017 that future wars will be fought by drones, and that once one side has seen its drones destroyed by those of another, it will have no choice but to surrender. According to the online magazine, Korii, published on June 13, 2020, through the voice of the lieutenant general head of the Joint Artificial Intelligence Center, the Pentagon has announced that it plans, in July 2021, to test the war-fighting skills of an Artificial Intelligence in a "*kind of aerial combat*" between a human-piloted aircraft and a fully autonomous, AI-piloted F-16 fighter jet. The artificial pilot will be able to make rapid decisions by processing gigantic amounts of data in real time. Unlike a human, it will not be disturbed by physical and emotional sensations in hostile skies. It's worth noting that the Pentagon has announced the Skyborg program in 2019 to accelerate research into aeronautical Artificial Intelligences and their articulation with human thought. For over two decades, nations and aerospace manufacturers have entered a frantic race for these automated or AI-supported weapons systems, with varying degrees of human intervention in the process.

The battle against the global pandemic of the new coronavirus (Covid-19), which is a human tragedy and an international health crisis and poses major risks to the economy, is cruel and unforgettable. As part of international cooperation to combat the Covid-19 epidemic and ensure global health security, scientists are racing against time to find a cure for the new coronavirus (Covid-19). Numerous countries have joined the exchange of information on the various responses to the new coronavirus (Covid-19), described as the enemy of Mankind. Computer biologists are leading a project linking thousands of machines together to create a virtual supercomputer, claimed to be the world's most powerful computer, capable of performing trillions of calculations every second, which should help understand the structure of the coronavirus. The project is based at Washington University in St. Louis. The computer-aided drug design method has already found a target in the Ebola virus; the new coronavirus (Covid-19) has a similar structure to the SARS virus, which has been the subject of numerous studies. 77 potential compounds have been identified that could bind to the coronavirus' main protein to disarm the pathogen. Experimental therapies are systematically evaluated. This generates the solid data that the world of science and medicine needs, to show which treatments are the most effective. AI accelerates the search for treatments for the new coronavirus. It helps to think through the challenges of the new coronavirus. Humanity cannot overcome a major catastrophe or epidemic without scientific development and technological innovation, which Artificial Intelligence facilitates. In Ghana, a drone start-up from Silicon Valley, Zipline, which operates a fleet of drones to deliver blood, vaccines and medical supplies to rural areas, uses drones to collect Covid-19 test samples and bring them back to medical laboratories in the country's two biggest cities, Accra and Kumasi. All in less than an hour. Using the contactless drone to transport Covid-19 test samples enables the Government of Ghana to respond to the pandemic and save lives more quickly. On the other hand, containment and the new coronavirus crisis are having a strong emotional impact. At the start of the progressive de-confinement, a clinical psychologist and emotion specialist, Robert Zuili, declared in an interview with a 20 Minutes journalist, published on May 25, 2020: "*In our emotional functions, the crisis will leave a trace that can modify our relationship to the world*". He has designed an app and Artificial Intelligence to measure the impact of the coronavirus crisis on emotions. In July 2020, the WHO Director-General announced the creation of the Independent Pandemic Preparedness and Response Group (IPPRG) to assess the global response to the COVID-19 pandemic. In August 2020, several candidate vaccines against Covid-19, including four from China, began international Phase 3 clinical trials. Several countries have developed a series of measures to enable safe deployment of a future Covid-19 vaccine. In all countries, the start of the new school year has raised serious concerns about the risk of epidemic outbreaks in schools and universities. In China, for example, according to People's Daily online, with a mixture of nervousness and excitement, many students in China began a new school year on September 1er 2020. But there's less nervousness than in the first semester of 2020. Although the COVID-19 epidemic has clearly receded in China, schools at all levels have nevertheless taken strict anti-epidemic measures to protect students' health. In the field of Covid-19 vaccine supply, the Kingdom of Morocco has signed a cooperation agreement with the Chinese laboratory NCBG for clinical trials of the Covid-19 vaccine. The only condition set by the Chinese laboratory is that volunteers must not be suffering from a chronic disease that could affect the outcome of the vaccine. On September 18, 2020, in Rabat, the Moroccan Minister of Health signed a memorandum of understanding for the acquisition of Covid-19 vaccines produced by R-Pharm, under license from the AstraZeneca group. The signing, which took place by videoconference between the two parties, is part of the Kingdom's efforts to secure the country's supply of sufficient quantities of vaccines. Moroccan companies are contributing to the fight against Covid-19. For example, a company based in Fez has succeeded in designing and manufacturing ultraviolet radiation disinfection machines, using a fast, effective and inexpensive process. These UVC machines emit ultraviolet radiation via variable-wattage lamps. They use type C ultraviolet technology with a wavelength of 253 nanometers. According to a statement made by its managers in September 2020, this process, which meets a pressing need in these times of pandemic Covid-19, and which has proved its worth abroad, can "deeply" disinfect a medium-sized room in just fifteen minutes. The process is aimed at the medical sector (hospitals, clinics, care centers, analysis laboratories, pharmacies, etc.), schools, administrations and hotels.

Digital technologies, including cell phones, social media and Artificial Intelligence, can play an important role in the fight against pandemics, making it possible to monitor, anticipate and influence the spread of disease and human behavior. At a time of unprecedented health crisis, with the Covid-19 pandemic, new intelligent surveillance systems are being created around the world, by both governments and companies. The current crisis could mark a major turning point in the history of surveillance. Firstly, because it could legitimize and normalize the massive deployment of surveillance tools in countries that have previously rejected them. The second reason is even more important: this crisis could lead to a radical transition from "*on-skin*" to "*under-skin*" surveillance. Previously, governments and companies mainly monitored the actions of individuals, controlling where they go and whom they meet. Today, they are more interested in what goes on inside the individual's body: his or her state of health, temperature, blood pressure and so on. This kind of biometric information enables governments and companies to know much more about individuals than ever before.

The International Seminar on the Global Development of Science and Governance under the New Coronavirus Epidemic, with the theme "*Condensing Cooperative Consensus and Meeting Challenges Together*", held on May 30, 2020 in Beijing, is organized by the China Association for Science and Technology. The seminar is part of a series of international academic activities to celebrate the fourth National Science and Technology Workers' Day.

At a time when trade and logistical barriers are preventing the movement of essential goods, it is important to emphasize that science must be allowed to lead the global response to the Covid-19 pandemic. Man depends on science for survival. It helps us to better prevent and manage crises, and to ensure that we learn fully from what people are experiencing.

Intelligent science and technology covers a wider field, including Artificial Intelligence, robots, brain science and biological intelligence. Artificial Intelligence has very recently become a discipline in certain countries (China...). The recently established Mohamed bin Zayed University of Artificial Intelligence (MBZUAI), located in Abu Dhabi, is a research-led academic institution offering specialized degree programs to local and international students in the field of Artificial Intelligence. The creation of the Artificial Intelligence specialization reflects the demand for talent in human societies. The Artificial Intelligence specialization follows trends in social demand for talent in this sector.

UNESCO is the only specialized UN organization with a specific mission to promote science. International scientific programs are developed. Also within the UN system, the United Nations Conference on Trade and Development (UNCTAD), a subsidiary body of the UN General Assembly created in 1964, is responsible for all activities relating to investment and technology.

There are other bodies within the United Nations system dealing with issues relating to science, technology and innovation.

At the High-Level Meeting on the Impact of Rapid Technological Change on the Achievement of the Sustainable Development Goals (SDGs), held on June11, 2020, the UN Secretary-General said that managing rapid technological change is a defining challenge of the current generation. He stressed that the international community is at a turning point and must urgently harness the infinite possibilities offered by digital technology to intensify the efforts of all nations in healthcare, the climate crisis and poverty eradication, on the scale of the Sustainable Development Goals.He declared:
"New technologies open up promising horizons not only for the promotion of new-generation jobs, but also for the acceleration of international cooperation in the fields of open science, scientific research in particular, to found a new economy based on knowledge and creativity".

Every year, the monthly Times Higher Education (THE) provides the World University Rankings since the launch of its current methodology in 2011. This ranking is considered one of the most balanced and comprehensive in the world, with 13 distinct performance indicators covering the full range of traditional activities of the most research-intensive universities, including teaching, research, knowledge transfer and international outlook. The 2021 ranking analyzed over 86 million citations in more than 13.6 million research articles, as well as the results of a survey of over 22,000 researchers worldwide. Britain's Oxford University retains top spot for the fifth year running. Sidi Mohammed Ben Abdellah University (USMBA) in Fez consolidated its position at the top of the list of Moroccan universities for the third time in succession, according to the Times magazine's annual ranking for 2021.

The 2020 edition of the Global Innovation Index, launched on September 02, 2020, presents the latest global trends in innovation, as well as the annual innovation rankings of 131 countries. According to the Global Innovation Index 2020, Switzerland is the most innovative country in the world, followed by Sweden, the USA, the UK and the Netherlands. The Global Innovation Index appeals to economic and political leaders around the world to support innovation.

b) International law of scientific and technical research, and international cooperation in the fields of science, scientific and technological research and innovation

Science is by nature international. International scientific relations have a long history. International law is based on the belief in the primacy of the community interest. The international community is increasingly interested in scientific progress. International conventions on scientific and technical cooperation proliferated after the Second World War. Some establish privileged scientific and technical relations between two States. Others are multilateral, often giving rise to international organizations with a scientific purpose. In the field of nuclear security, for example, the international legal framework is made up of legal instruments and recognized principles designed to prevent, detect and respond to criminal or other unauthorized acts involving or targeting nuclear materials, other radioactive materials, and related facilities or activities.

Since the 1950s, the United Nations has been promoting the use of science and technology for the development of its Member States. The Commission on Science and Technology for Development (CSTD), created in 1992 and attached to the United Nations Economic and Social Council (ECOSOC), is the forum for debate on science and technology. The rapid pace of technological change, the problems it poses and the promises it holds are at the heart of discussions within this Commission, among others. The Commission is also responsible for coordinating follow-up to the World Summit on the Information Society. The Commission on Science and Technology for Development (CSTD) plays its role as a forum for the examination of issues relating to science and technology, for a better understanding of science and technology policies for development, and for the elaboration of recommendations and guidelines concerning science and technology issues within the United Nations system, all with a view to development. The twenty-second session of the CSTD took place in Geneva from May 13 to 17, 2019. It addressed, among other issues, the impact of rapid technological change on sustainable development, and the role of science, technology and innovation (STI) in building resilient human societies, including through the contribution of "*citizen science*".

UNCTAD provides secretariat services to the Commission on Science and Technology for Development. It helps developing countries review their science and technology policies, and provides technical assistance in the field of information technology. UNCTAD works to ensure that new technologies are at the service of all countries and all individuals - that is, that they improve their daily lives while respecting their rights.

The International Bioethics Committee (IBC), set up in 1993, is made up of 36 independent experts. These experts oversee the progress of life science research and its applications, while ensuring respect for the principles of human dignity and freedom. The International Bioethics Committee is the only global body for reflection on bioethical issues. The Intergovernmental Bioethics Committee (IGBC) was created in 1998, in accordance with article 11 of the statutes of the International Bioethics Committee (IBC). It is made up of 36 member states, whose representatives meet at least once every two years to examine the advice and recommendations of the IBC. It informs the IBC of its point of view and submits its opinions, together with its proposals concerning the follow-up to be given to the advice and recommendations of the IBC, to the Director-General of UNESCO for transmission to the Member States, the Executive Board and the General Conference. The World Commission on the Ethics of Scientific Knowledge and Technology (COMEST), created in 1998 by UNESCO, is an advisory body and a forum for reflection. It is made up of eminent specialists in scientific, legal, philosophical, cultural and political disciplines from various regions of the world, 18 of whom are appointed by the Director-General of UNESCO in their individual capacities. The role of this Commission (COMEST) is to enunciate ethical principles likely to enlighten the debates of political leaders in the light of criteria that are not strictly economic.

The World Summit on Sustainable Development, held in September 2015, launched the Technology Facilitation Mechanism for the achievement of the Sustainable Development Goals provided for in the Addis Ababa Action Agenda and the United Nations 2030 Agenda for Sustainable Development. This Mechanism includes, among others, the annual multi-stakeholder Collaboration Forum on Science, Technology and Innovation (STI) for the Sustainable Development Goals, which meets once a year at global level.

The Technology Facilitation Mechanism for the achievement of the Sustainable Development Goals demonstrates that Member States have recognized the fundamental importance of the "science, technology and innovation" sector for the achievement of sustainable development. The third Multistakeholder Collaboration Forum on Science, Technology and Innovation for the Achievement of the Sustainable Development Goals, on the theme: "*Science, Technology and Innovation for Sustainable and Resilient Societies - Focus on SDGs 6, 7, 11, 12 and 15*", was held on 05 and 06 June 2018. On 1ère day, the Group of 77 and China saw the Forum as a platform for exchanges between developed and developing countries. It focused on the use of science, technology and innovation in five areas of action: strengthening basic social services, bridging the digital and technological divide, building the capacities of developing countries, remedying the problems of these countries' technological structures, and developing, disseminating and transferring technology to them on favorable terms. For the least developed countries (LDCs), which do not have the capacity to acquire cutting-edge technologies, we need to ensure that the fourth digital revolution does not lead to a widening of the technological gap or to massive job losses, which robotization and Artificial Intelligence could cause. This is one of the conclusions of the Clearing House's report: with technological change, new jobs are created while others are abolished. On **the** second day of the third Forum, the Science and Technology Advisor to Japan's Ministry of Foreign Affairs said:

" *we want to create society 5.0, a participatory society centered on the human being, achieved by the fusion of cybernetic and physical space*".

The Fourth Multistakeholder Collaboration Forum on Science, Technology and Innovation (STI) for Sustainable Development Goals, on the theme "*Science, Technology and Innovation for Inclusiveness and Equality*", was held on May 14 and 15, 2019, under the auspices of the Economic and Social Council (ECOSOC). On the first day, the UN Under-Secretary-General for Economic and Social Affairs emphasized that science, technology and innovation (STI) are necessary to find solutions in all sectors and crucial to achieving the Sustainable Development Goals. The representative of the UN Department of Economic and Social Affairs called for the facilitation of technologies to combat inequalities that could be exacerbated, with the risk of many finding themselves trapped, in the long term, in the "*low-tech trap*". He also spoke of the impact of automated production and Artificial Intelligence on development, noting that these tools can accelerate the downward trend in operational costs and the use of workers across a wide range of sectors. The representative of the UN Department of Economic and Social Affairs noted that

"Many countries will therefore have to rethink their development trajectory in order to integrate these new technologies, and rethink their approaches to jobs, inclusion, income distribution and the social contract".

One of the four interactive debates focused on the importance of data, the "*black gold*" of our times. One delegate pointed out that the accumulation of data has reached unprecedented levels, but that it is concentrated on a limited number of computer networks and clouds, in the hands of a small number of people. This is an unprecedented situation, with practical implications for the use and allocation of resources. One of the conclusions **of the** first day was that digital technologies, such as Artificial Intelligence, automation, biotechnology and nanotechnology, are having a considerable impact on the economy, human societies and the environment, and that efforts are needed to prevent them from further widening the digital divide. On the second day of the fourth Forum, many speakers stressed the importance of capacity-building and technology transfer to the countries of the South, while others were quick to point out the possible drawbacks of technology. The Head of the Secretariat of the United Nations Permanent Forum on Indigenous Issues pointed out that to say that indigenous peoples have millennia of knowledge does not mean that they are "*stuck in the past*". She pointed out that these peoples continue to create and innovate today, drawing precisely on this millennia-old knowledge. Raising the issue of inclusion of people with disabilities, the representative of CBM, International Advocacy and Alliances, noted that Artificial Intelligence and robotics, which are changing the way people work, are particularly useful for this purpose. Despite the progress, she deplored the fact that the disabled continue to face the problem of exclusion and are marginalized. The interesting and instructive debates highlighted what is possible when innovators put their creativity and talent at the service of the Sustainable Development Goals.

Science, Technology and Innovation Forum showcases creativity and talent in support of the Sustainable Development Goals. Due to the Covid-19 pandemic, the Forum on Science, Technology and Innovation for the Sustainable Development Goals, scheduled for May 12-13, 2020 in New York, has been postponed until the 2021 session of ECOSOC. It should be noted that there is, moreover, the African Regional Forum on Science, Technology and Innovation, created by Resolution (LI) of the ECA Conference of Ministers dated May 15, 2018. The mission of this Regional Forum is to contribute to the work of the African Regional Forum for Sustainable Development and the Multistakeholder Forum on Science, Technology and Innovation for the Sustainable Development Goals. The first meeting of the African Regional Forum on Science, Technology and Innovation was held **on** April 16, 2019 in Marrakech. At this session, participants addressed opportunities around scaling up actions by considering the role STI can play in accelerating efforts to achieve the SDGs.

c) **The digital revolution and its impact on the economy:** transforming lifestyles, working methods, economic development and new technologies.

Science and technology bring benefits to economies, development and human societies.

The drivers of change vary over time. We are witnessing different technological revolutions and industrial transformations. Today's technological advances differ from those of the past. Innovation cycles are faster. Technological evolution and the resulting obsolescence of skills affect almost all workers. Scientific and technical advances have given rise to the digital revolution. The word "*digital*" refers to the process of digitizing an ever-increasing amount of information. Digital encompasses information technology, but its scope is broader, as it also covers telecommunications: telephone, radio, television, computer and Internet. The process of digitization is reflected in the evolution of all kinds of tools that are dramatically transforming social links. These tools are becoming more numerous and more powerful. The term "digital technologies" covers a wide range of technologies based on the interpretation of information coded in a binary format, which are an inescapable aspect of modern life and are at the heart of innovation in all sectors of society. These technologies are increasingly used in smart city projects, industrial control systems and personal objects and devices. The increased use of ever more sophisticated, complex and interconnected digital technologies has given rise to new vulnerabilities and led to the creation of harmful IT tools. These vulnerabilities and tools can be exploited by people with a variety of purposes, including crime and terrorism, and by states seeking to strengthen their military capabilities.

Information and communication technologies (ICT), a sub-category of digital technologies, encompass a diverse set of tools and resources used to transmit, store, create, share or exchange information, particularly via the Internet. The increasing use of these technologies is driven by advances in networking, data science, cloud computing and the Internet of Things. ICTs are becoming increasingly complex, both in terms of software and hardware. They are spreading to all sectors of human society, bringing about profound changes. Opportunities are associated with them.

The World IT Congress 2019 was held on September 10 and 11, 2019 in Changsha, capital of the central province of Hunan. Experts and company representatives from around the world gathered at the event to exchange views on the future trend of IT technologies and industries. The Congress highlighted Artificial Intelligence and other recent technologies. Nine forums were held on topics including 5G, AI algorithms and network security. The IT industry worldwide is facing unprecedented opportunities and challenges.

Human memory is fallible. Thanks to computers, the purely mechanical functions of the brain, such as memory, are externalized. Having a good memory, learning everything by heart, is no longer a necessity, since the computer's memory is far greater than that of the user. Freed from this constraint, the brain uses its other functions, and can thus deploy its creativity. This creativity will enable mankind to be more inventive and intelligent, and to play an active role in this new period in history.

Human societies and lifestyles are undergoing changes, the scale and speed of which are largely due to the disruptions brought about by information and communications technologies. The availability in digital form of a considerable mass of information of all kinds (personal, professional, public...) has led to the important notions, among others, of Open Data. Digitization is fuelling the rise of 3D printing, Artificial Intelligence, the Internet of Things, cloud computing, Big Data and automation. The current period is one of radical innovation. For governments, institutions and businesses, the creation, control and exploitation of information are a strategic, societal, cultural, economic and technological challenge. Digital technologies bring power, speed and ease to the acquisition, management and exchange of numbers, text, images and sound.

Digital technologies are changing economies, public administrations and human societies, and influencing development. Digital transformation is often associated with collaboration in processes, working methods and innovation. The digitization of the economy opens up new opportunities for businesses and others, while creating significant benefits for consumers. It has an impact on all aspects of production and commerce. Digitization is leading to restructuring within organizations. It not only eliminates jobs, but also creates new ones. The digitization of economic activities has accelerated thanks to the expansion of broadband access and the drastic reduction in the cost of ICT equipment and software. The speed of digital transformation varies from country to country. The digital economy is booming in developing countries.

Digital technologies are rapidly transforming human societies. Their emergence has improved the human condition to an unprecedented degree, but it has also given rise to profound new challenges. The limitless possibilities offered by the application of digital technologies go hand in hand with flagrant abuses and unintended consequences. Digital dividends and fractures coexist.

The development of information and communication technologies is progressing and influencing the development of all other sectors of the economy. New technologies have generally resulted in cheaper, higher-quality products, leading to increased consumer demand and job creation. But technological progress can exacerbate income inequalities. The digital world allows "*digital innovators*" to advance rapidly in winner-take-all markets.

Emerging technologies are transforming the management of institutions and companies, and the challenges they face. Many organizations are less reliant on a core workforce, as they can draw on the power of participative working and the online workforce. Tasks performed by humans are increasingly being replaced by machine learning algorithms. In the near future, there will be more emerging technologies at work, such as robots, 3D printers, mobile technologies and smart objects. Emerging technologies will transform the way objects are designed, produced and distributed, just as the Internet has changed organizational practices. These technologies are expected to go beyond the digital world to create objects and environments that are smarter, more operational, more interconnected and more universal.

The UN makes the case for a safer, more inclusive digital future. Following its creation in July 2018 by the UN Secretary-General, the 20-person High-Level Panel on Digital Cooperation published its report entitled "*The era of digital interdependence*" on June 10, 2019. The Group was created in response to the UN Secretary-General's wish to involve the private sector, including industry, Governments, academia, civil society and intergovernmental organizations in efforts to meet the challenges of the digital age. In presenting the report, the authors presented a "*Declaration of Digital Interdependence*", which describes Humanity as currently "*at the wall*" *of* the digital age and facing risks, such as misuse by private companies, failure to realize human potential and crippling but necessary regulation. The report explored the contribution that digital technology can make to achieving the 2030 Agenda for Sustainable Development, the links between digital technology, human rights and security, and models for digital cooperation between different parts of society. In its report, the High-Level Group called for
"the strengthening of multi-stakeholder digital cooperation to reflect on the design and application

of standards and principles such as transparency and non-partiality in autonomous intelligent systems in different social contexts".

It suggested a first goal for the 75ème anniversary of the United Nations in 2020, namely the development of a "*Global Commitment to Digital Cooperation*" that would enshrine the shared values, principles, understandings and goals for an enhanced global digital cooperation architecture. The High Level Group believes

"*to a future where enhanced digital cooperation supports the achievement of the Sustainable Development Goals, reduces inequalities, brings people closer together, strengthens international peace and security, and promotes economic opportunity and environmental sustainability*".

He hoped

"*that this report and its recommendations will be part of the building blocks of an inclusive and interdependent digital world, with a new and adapted governance architecture*".

In addition, the UN Secretary-General also addressed an informal meeting of the General Assembly at UN headquarters on the same day, June 10, 2019, during which he urged member states to study the report closely and expressed the hope that it would stimulate

"*an urgent and open debate between Governments, the private sector, civil society and others on how we move forward together securely in the age of digital interdependence*".

The Secretary-General stated that

"*the international community is failing to assume its responsibilities. The governance systems for digital technology are old, fragmented and reactive. The longer we wait to update these systems, the further behind we will fall*".

On May 29, 2020, the UN Secretary-General released his Report entitled "*Digital Cooperation Action Plan: implementing the recommendations of the High-Level Panel on Digital Cooperation*". This Report responds to the recommendations of the High-Level Panel on Digital Cooperation on key issues such as universal connectivity, digital inclusion, human rights, Artificial Intelligence, and the promotion of digital trust and security. In his report, the Secretary-General assesses the current state of digital cooperation, particularly in the light of the ongoing coronavirus pandemic (COVID-19), while also analyzing gaps and urgent challenges, and outlining measures to strengthen global digital cooperation. With regard to Artificial Intelligence, the Report states that the Secretary-General intends to

"to create a multi-stakeholder advisory body on global cooperation on Artificial Intelligence so that I and the international community have guidance on artificial intelligence in a way that is reliable, human rights-based, safe and sustainable, and promotes peace. This advisory body will include Member States, relevant UN entities, interested companies, academic institutions and civil society groups".

He pointed out that this

"organ could also serve as a diverse forum to share and promote best practices as well as exchange views on AI standardization and compliance efforts, while taking into account existing mandates and institutions."

The Global Digital Economy 2020 Conference and Smart City and Economy Trade Fair is being held from September 11 to 13, 2020 in Ningbo, Zhejiang province. With the theme of "digital facilitating smart development", the fair has focused on important areas of the digital economy, such as 5G technology, megadata, Artificial Intelligence (AI), the Industrial Internet and smart manufacturing, aiming to integrate innovative resources for a new era of the digital economy. The show will also feature four competitions on Artificial Intelligence, Industrial Internet and other relevant industries. During the show, competitions on Artificial Intelligence and Industrial Internet, among others, will be held. The show has attracted the attention of relevant industries and has become a platform for cooperation and communication for the digital economy sector. Ningbo is currently implementing a new action plan for the digital economy, promising to become an exemplary city at the forefront of industrial Internet development and international intelligent manufacturing. Under the influence of the Covid-19 epidemic, Zhejiang has created a precision intelligence control system, which has promoted the integrated development of the digital economy in various fields. It is committed to implementing digital economy construction, breaking through in core technologies and continuously improving its demonstration and outreach role in the digital economy.

Technological change is accelerating, but digital cooperation and governance mechanisms have failed to keep pace. In an age of digital interdependence, the dynamic digital world urgently needs better digital cooperation. This cooperation must be based on shared human values, such as inclusion, respect, humanism, human rights, international law, transparency and sustainability. These shared values must become a common light that illuminates the path ahead. Effective digital cooperation requires a strengthening of multilateralism, despite current tensions. It also requires complementing this multilateralism with multi-stakeholder cooperation: cooperation that involves not only governments, but also a much more diverse range of other stakeholders such as civil society, academics, technologists and the private sector. Far more diverse voices must be heard, and we must work to build an inclusive and interdependent digital world, with a new and adapted governance architecture.

Innovation can only thrive if we promote a digital culture. Digital transformation facilitates the integration of Artificial Intelligence solutions. To be able to integrate AI systems, however, we need both agile, digitized processes and an awareness of Data among employees.

The challenges posed by the current wave of digitization are enormous. The key is to ride the wave of digitization successfully.

d) Links between the digital revolution and development

Digital technologies are rapidly transforming human societies. Digitization is global, affecting every aspect of life. Communication technologies have transformed the way people live and the way countries develop. They offer communities the opportunity to solve many of the major problems they face. Literacy and digital skills are crucial factors for social and personal improvement and progress, as well as for promoting entrepreneurship and building strong digital economies. Digital technologies offer the potential for sustainability and environmental protection.

Digital technologies make an important contribution to achieving sustainable development. The Sustainable Development Goals (SDGs) make explicit mention of digital technologies on five occasions: i) SDG #4 on education, ii) SDG #5 on gender equality, iii) SDG #8 on decent work and economic growth, iv) SDG #9 on industry, innovation and infrastructure, and v) SDG #17 on partnerships. The SDGs emphasize that providing universal and affordable access to the Internet to people in the least developed countries by 2020 will be crucial to fostering their development, as the rise of the digital economy could be an engine for decent employment and inclusive growth as well as increased exports and their diversification. Advanced technologies open up new avenues for building resilience, which is decisive for sustainable development. ICTs have been decisive for growth in recent years. In its Resolution A/RES/70/125, the United Nations General Assembly, in its global assessment of the implementation of the outcomes of the World Summit on the Information Society, committed itself to harnessing the potential of ICTs to achieve the goals of the 2030 Agenda for Sustainable Development and the other internationally agreed development goals, indicating that ICTs could accelerate the progress expected across all 17 SDGs.

The emergence of digital technologies has improved the human condition to an unprecedented degree, but it has also given rise to profound new challenges. Digitization is creating more and more monopolies, and posing new challenges for antitrust and competition policies in both developed and developing countries. Connectivity remains a challenge and a concern, at the root of various digital divides in both access to and use of ICTs.

The world is debating how to ensure a safe and inclusive digital future that takes account of relevant human rights standards. Cooperation across domains and borders is essential to harness the socio-economic potential of these technologies, mitigate the risks they pose and prevent any unintended outcomes.

In 2018, UNESCO published the Internet Universality Indicators. Its document creates a framework of indicators to assess the level of realization, in each country, of the four DOAM principles included in the concept of Internet Universality, according to which the Internet must be based on human rights (D), must be open (O), accessible to all (A) and must be powered by multi-stakeholder participation (M).

Humanitarian innovation must be compatible with humanitarian principles (humanity, impartiality, neutrality and independence) and the principle of dignity. It must be carried out with the aim of promoting the rights, dignity and capabilities of the beneficiary population, and all members of a crisis-affected community must be able to benefit from the innovation without discriminatory barriers to use. Risk analysis and mitigation must be used to prevent unintended harm, including that related to privacy and data security, as well as impacts on local economies. Innovation must also be geared towards managing the most perilous problems the planet has ever faced, such as climate change.

e) The rise of Artificial Intelligence (AI) technologies

It's interesting to know about the company's origins and history, in order to understand its initial directions and future prospects.

The first milestones in the history of Artificial Intelligence (AI) date back to the dawn of time, when myths and legends, recounted in stories told by traditional communities such as the Imazighanes, endowed imaginary characters with extraordinary intelligence, even superior to that of humans. In modern times, Artificial Intelligence (AI) has become widely popularized in the world of science fiction.

Before exploring the transformational opportunities and challenges associated with deploying AI systems in urban environments, it is important to define and contextualize this complex notion. It is also important to analyze the dynamics of the rise of Artificial Intelligence: its speed and scale, the forces shaping it, its political economy and its key global players.

Intelligence has many facets. Its definition is complex and controversial. It varies with the times, the thinkers and the discoveries about how it works. There are many definitions of Artificial Intelligence. The limits of the definition are not clearly defined. Broadly speaking, Artificial Intelligence (AI) is the science of having a machine perform tasks that humans perform using their intelligence and cognitive abilities. It's a multitude of techniques and technologies that respond to challenges with adapted solutions. In particular, these techniques call on the use of computers, electronics, mathematics (especially statistics), neuroscience and cognitive science. Artificial Intelligence technologies can simulate human intelligence and automatically perform perception, comprehension and decision-making tasks. The aim of Artificial Intelligence is to simulate human behavior on computer systems.

As early as 1950, Alan Turing, the British mathematician and pioneering computer theorist whose work laid the scientific foundations of computing, refocused the debate on Artificial Intelligence with the "*Turing Test*". He suggested replacing the question "*Can machines think?*" with "*Can machines imitate human intelligence?*". Alan Turing proposed testing the ability of machines to imitate human conversation through written questions and answers. In 1956, at the Dartmouth Conference, the term "*Artificial Intelligence*" was used for the first time, following the birth of the artificial neuron in 1943. This conference created a new discipline. *It pointed* the way to neural networks, machine learning and the study of creativity. Research then focused on these and other avenues. AI research really began after this conference. AI technologies are the result of a complex interplay of disciplines, including logic and mathematics. Artificial Intelligence is a theoretical and practical interdisciplinary field whose aim is to understand the mechanisms of cognition and thought, and to imitate them through hardware and software devices, in order to assist or replace human activities. It has a shifting frontier, in line with scientific progress and human perception of so-called "*intelligent*" tasks. AI projects are carried out by multidisciplinary research teams.

Artificial Intelligence takes a number of forms: intelligent conversational robots, AI-powered recommendation engines, and so on. AI technologies can improve iteratively as expertise and data availability develop. Among other things, they can support business processes by automating reasoning that can be simulated in algorithms. The gains in speed and efficiency are considerable.

Algorithms and Artificial Intelligence are everywhere. They are closely linked. An algorithm is a sequence of operations or instructions to obtain a result. In many ways, a recipe is an algorithm. The operation of many tools is based on algorithms. Algorithms come in many forms. In an algorithm, there is a risk of bias at every stage. The bias of an algorithm is the gap between what the algorithm says and reality. In some cases, these biases can lead to discrimination. Biases **are** very often due to the data used. AI algorithms are taking center stage, with the corollary need to audit them given the risks announced in terms of ethics, biases and black boxes. Moreover, the use of AI algorithms without ethical reflection and control can generate major risks on a large scale. The challenge is to detect bias in algorithms and create fair algorithms. It is necessary to ensure that, in the AI process, each link in the chain implements good practices to prevent, detect and warn of possible biases. It is necessary to define the methodological requirements for ensuring algorithm quality, the analyses and evaluations that the algorithm must undergo, and the properties that the algorithms developed must have.

Artificial Intelligence (AI) programming has evolved with advances in computer science and discoveries in neuroscience. The technical landscape of Artificial Intelligence has metamorphosed since 1950. It has evolved over the decades. Three trends are converging: i) Big Data, ii) machine learning and iii) Cloud supercomputing. Machine learning refers to the activity of algorithms capable of automatically sorting complex patterns from very large datasets, via supervised or unsupervised learning. The convergence of two branches of machine learning has produced impressive results: deep learning and reinforced learning. Deep learning technology is a system of automatic learning algorithms used, for example, to decipher an image or understand a conversation. It uses an architecture of interconnected artificial neurons, inspired by that of the brain. This network is capable of processing large quantities of information and learning progressively from images, texts or data. It learns to represent the world. With deep learning, the machine learns to do this itself. And it does it much better than engineers. Deep learning *is* the most promising technology in machine learning. Its capabilities continue to be explored, with a recent paradigm shift opening up exciting prospects. Research is also being carried out into neuromorphic computing, an experimental field in which the aim is to make computers work like human brains when processing information. We take the real brain process and put it into silicon. With neuromorphic processors, the possibilities for Artificial Intelligence systems take on a whole new dimension. American processor manufacturer Intel Inc. has developed a neuromorphic computing system capable of emulating the equivalent of 100 million neurons. In collaboration with Cornell University, Intel's Neuromorphic Computing Laboratory has developed a "*digital nose*", trained to mimic the olfactory system of animals.

The rise of Artificial Intelligence is indeed a manifestation of the digital revolution. AI has progressed thanks to the systematic use of data, but modeling makes it easier to understand causality. Excellence is based on, among other things, research into theoretical algorithms, human and cognitive sciences, a large database and a willingness to combine the "*scientific*" with the "*political*". Artificial Intelligence is supported by a strong IT industry. Data is the cornerstone of AI, and its very lifeblood. Thanks to digitalization, mankind is storing data at an exponential rate. It's worth pointing out that data is at the heart of the digital age, whether it's big (Big Data), not so big

(Smart Data) or small (Small Data). But the "*black box*" effect is a risk, especially at a time when it is essential to control how decisions are made or assisted by the machine.

AI technologies, both fantasized and feared, are being used in a growing number of solutions that address complex issues of safety, mobility or citizenship, improve the quality of public services, address urgent challenges, deliver significant productivity gains and enable social advances, including food supply, improved health, increased labor market participation, safeguarding human rights, achieving gender equality, empowering seniors and people with disabilities, eradicating harmful prejudice and supporting inclusive human societies.

The advent of the digital society, the omnipotence of "*Big Data*", the increasing storage capacity and computing power of computers, and the sophistication of processing and analysis algorithms are creating the conditions for the exponential development of Artificial Intelligence. According to an article published in Le Figaro on June 23, 2020, a Japanese supercomputer is shaking up the Sino-American race for computing power. This Japanese supercomputer, named Fugaku and developed jointly by the Riken research institute and Fujitsu for 1 billion dollars, dominates all its competitors. Based on ARM chips, it is almost three times faster than the Summit system manufactured by American IBM, its closest rival. Its power of 415.53 petaflops enables it to calculate at a speed of 415 million billion operations per second. The machine, which won't be fully operational until 2021, will also be able to forecast the weather with unrivalled accuracy. According to the Chinese People's Daily online of June 30, 2020, Chinese manufacturers continue to dominate the list of the world's fastest supercomputer manufacturers in terms of number of systems, according to Top500, an authoritative ranking of supercomputers worldwide.

Supercomputers installed by three Chinese suppliers - Lenovo, Sugon and Inspur - account for 312 of the top 500 systems in the 55ème edition of the Top500 supercomputer list. At a press conference held on September 16, 2020 by the Information Office of the State Council -the Chinese Government-, the President of the Chinese Academy of Sciences indicated that the Academy will focus on, among other things, supercomputing systems. He stated that

"As *China faces a transformation of science and technology to meet the country's high-quality economic development standards, and as it faces pressure from US high-tech companies, we hope to do more to help solve critical problems in these aspects over the next 10 years.*"

Moreover, advances in Artificial Intelligence are impacting all sectors. At a time when digital technology is transforming companies and institutions, Artificial Intelligence is poised to revolutionize the way they operate. Artificial Intelligence is opening up new avenues for economic growth. Innovations in AI technologies could create new sources of economic growth, especially in economies largely dependent on traditional production levers. More and more tasks performed by humans will be automated, requiring new skills to complement AI technologies. Artificial Intelligence, which fosters economic growth, societal trust, gender equality and inclusion, is dependent on a predictable and stable political environment conducive to innovation.

Scientists are making great strides in the development of Artificial Intelligence technologies and applications. Artificial Intelligence is an integral part of the technological revolution the world is currently experiencing. Artificial Intelligence offers opportunities to advance sustainable development for human progress. The transformative power of Artificial Intelligence is nonetheless accompanied by complex challenges: issues of trust, fears of exacerbating inequalities, and so on. It should be noted that it is the representation of the world that researchers present to algorithms, in the form of data; the intentions of humans are behind these programs that guide decision-making processes. It is therefore vital that this data can be controlled, anonymized and made as neutral as possible, to avoid biased representations of the world.

Artificial Intelligence is taking off and beginning to infiltrate people's daily lives, among other things. It is set to profoundly transform their relationship with technology. Its development is currently very dynamic. The USA and China are two behemoths vying for global supremacy in Artificial Intelligence. China is working to overtake the USA by 2025 and become world leader by 2030. Breaking with the diplomatic caution of Deng Xiaoping, Chinese President Xi Jinping is working to bring China back to the forefront of the international stage as an undisputed power. To this end, he intends to harness the development of Artificial Intelligence.

China attaches great importance to the development of Artificial Intelligence. Chinese President Xi Jinping's objective is to create a vast military-industrial complex, along the lines of DARPA, aimed at making China a future center of innovation in Artificial Intelligence. To this end, China is playing a key role in creating an economic, legal and political ecosystem conducive to potential technological breakthroughs in the field of AI. In 2017, the State Council published the "*Next-Generation Artificial Intelligence Development Plan*" proposing a comprehensive deployment of the system in terms of development objectives, development priorities. As part of the implementation of this Plan, China, which is a fast-growing country in Artificial Intelligence work and research, is investing heavily to develop a new generation of AI technologies. It has initiated two groups of major projects on next-generation AI technologies. These major projects target AI technologies that are in world-leading fields and in line with the country's strategic needs. To facilitate the development of next-generation AI, China's Ministry of Science and Technology has made systematic arrangements ranging from studies on fundamental theories, key technologies, supporting systems and industrial applications. Support is focused on five scientific research themes: data intelligence, swarm intelligence, intermedia intelligence, human-machine hybrid intelligence and intelligent system. A team of 12 Chinese Artificial Intelligence company founders and researchers published a paper entitled "Towards a New Generation of Artificial Intelligence in China" in Nature Machine Intelligence in June 2020 to introduce and discuss the development of China's Artificial Intelligence industry and the country's programs for the sector, marking the first time Chinese experts have published an article on the topic of Artificial Intelligence in a prestigious global academic journal. Published monthly since January 2019, Nature Machine Intelligence is a thematic branch of the highly acclaimed scientific journal Nature. It covers research into artificial intelligence, machine learning and robotics. It's worth noting that in China, according to Science and Technology Daily, the 500-meter Aperture Spherical Telescope (FAST), a Chinese scientific megaproject and the world's largest dish radio observatory, has embarked on a search for forms of extraterrestrial intelligence. FAST, officially unveiled in September 2016, can detect radio waves billions of light-years away. The search for extraterrestrial intelligence is one of FAST's five main scientific objectives.

China's Artificial Intelligence industry is showing stronger innovation capabilities, with world-class applied technologies including image recognition and voice recognition. Intelligent technology has seen faster applications in manufacturing, transportation, healthcare, education and other fields. Promoting the integration of artificial intelligence and the real economy is an important way to optimize and upgrade industries and improve human well-being, and China encourages domestic and foreign enterprises and research institutes to deepen cooperation and jointly promote Artificial Intelligence technologies. Smart China Expo Online 2020, themed "Intelligent Technology: Empowering the Economy, Enriching Life", is being held from September 15 to 17, 2020, in the municipality of Chongqing (southwest China). At the exhibition, the Vice Minister of Industry and Information Technology said that by the end of 2019, the size of China's Artificial Intelligence industry had reached 51 billion yuan ($7.5 billion), with the number of companies in the sector exceeding 2,600. Smart China Expo Online serves as a platform to promote global exchanges of smart technologies and international cooperation in the smart industry.

AI is an inevitable process in the future development of next-generation computing technology, and it is also a direction of deep integration of computing technology and economic and social development that is attracting the world's interest.

The rise of Artificial Intelligence, following on from that of digital technology, is reshuffling the cards in the economy, particularly in industry, at a time when human societies are questioning the race for productivity and the need to produce and consume differently. Artificial Intelligence continues to evolve at a rapid pace. The world is being propelled into a new era of Artificial Intelligence.

Artificial Intelligence's meteoric development has placed it at the heart of issues relating to national sovereignty and security. In the USA, the then Secretary of Defense, Chuck Hagel, introduced the concept of the "*third strategic revolution*" ("*third offset strategy*") in 2014. This concept refers to the plan to create a third breakthrough after nuclear deterrence and the explosion of new information technologies. Artificial Intelligence will be associated with, but also integrated into, hypervelocity, submarine warfare and electronic warfare. The Russian Federation has long been involved in Artificial Intelligence and robotic technologies. Its cyberspace doctrine, formulated on September 09, 2000, was revised on December 05, 2016. The Russian Federation's doctrinal corpus has been supplemented over the years by several official texts. The Russian Federation has drawn up the Strategy for the Development of the Information Technology Industry for 2014-2020 and Outlook to 2025. It recently drew up the Strategy for the Development of the Information Society 2017-2030. In the midst of his re-election campaign, against a backdrop of great tension with his Western counterparts, in a speech to representatives of both Chambers and members of the Medvedev-led Government, Putin confirmed, on March 1er 2018, the Russian Federation's determination to ensure its military security through the development of various weapons... but, also, of Artificial Intelligence. The oukaze (law) setting out the framework, objectives and means for the development of Artificial Intelligence in Russia is enacted on October 10, 2019. Russian President Vladimir Putin took part in a high-profile public debate on Artificial Intelligence Day in Moscow on November 09, 2019. The European Commission, meanwhile, unveiled, on February 19, 2020, its ideas and measures for a digital transformation that benefits everyone, reflecting the best of what Europe offers: openness, fairness, diversity, democracy and trust. Today, she presented Europe's data strategy and options for action to ensure the development of human-centered Artificial Intelligence. In its white paper presented on the same day, the European Commission indicated that Europe has all the necessary assets to become a world leader in the development of Artificial Intelligence systems conducive to safe uses and applications. On June 09, 2020, the Council of the European Union adopted "*conclusions*" entitled "*Shaping Europe's digital future*", in which it addresses a wide range of issues related to the implementation of the

European Union's (EU) digital strategy. The areas covered by these *"conclusions" include* connectivity, digital value chains, Artificial Intelligence, e-Health, the data economy and digital platforms. In addition, these "*conclusions*" highlight the impact of digital transformation in the fight against the pandemic, as well as its essential role in the post-Covid-19 recovery.

In Turkey, the government has recently set its sights on transforming the economy into a knowledge-based economy based on the development of high-tech products with high added value. It has focused on pioneering technologies: cyber-physical systems, Artificial Intelligence systems, sensors, robotics technology, the Internet of Things, Big Data, cybersecurity and the Cloud. Turkey aims to keep pace with today's technological challenges. To meet the need for skilled manpower in the public and private sectors in the field of Artificial Intelligence, the first AI engineering department in Turkey opened its doors, in 2019, at Hacettepe University. The academic importance of AI is mentioned in the 2019 Higher Education Programs and Quotas Guide of the Center for Measurement, Selection and Placement (ÖSYM), in the "*Professions of the Future*" section. AI will become increasingly important in the coming years in Turkey. In the MENA region, when it comes to Artificial Intelligence, the United Arab Emirates stand out. They have been investing in Artificial Intelligence for several years. The UAE dreams of itself as an AI hub in the same way that its Dubai airport has become a hotspot for air transport between Europe and Asia. In October 2017, they launched a National Council for Artificial Intelligence and Blockchain, responsible for implementing these two technologies across all sectors. In 2017, the United Arab Emirates also created a State Ministry **of** Artificial Intelligence. The first of its kind in the world. In addition, an ambitious BRAIN (Build a Responsible Artificial Intelligence Nation) strategic plan is being unveiled in April 2019; this plans to make the UAE one of the leaders in AI by 2031. The UAE is looking to Artificial Intelligence as a way to diversify its economy. Artificial Intelligence has become their black gold. On April 30 and May 1er 2019 in Dubai, the United Arab Emirates organized a trade show dedicated to this technology: AI Everything. In October 2019, they announced the creation of the Mohamed bin Zayed University of Artificial Intelligence (MBZUAI). This is the world's first university dedicated to Artificial Intelligence and research. It will enable graduate students, companies and governments to progress in Artificial Intelligence.

The market for Artificial Intelligence technologies is flourishing.

Realizing the vast potential of AI technologies will require relevant investments in education, research, entrepreneurship and the labor market to promote skills and knowledge relevant to the jobs of the future and to adapt to changes in skills demand. Realizing this vast potential will require relevant investments in education, research, entrepreneurship and the labor market to promote skills and knowledge relevant to the jobs of the future, and to meet societal impacts and expectations of the new skills required. More and more tasks performed by humans will be automated, requiring new skills to complement AI technologies.

f) Combining Artificial Intelligence technologies with other new technologies

New technologies, especially digital technologies, which are often described as disruptive, and which have a huge impact on current economies and existing production systems, can be combined. These combinations then open up completely new possibilities, previously unimaginable.

Technological evolution will continue. New technologies will be used en masse for increasingly scientific training. The combination of Artificial Intelligence technologies, which reproduce the human cognition that permeates all human activities, with other new technologies, particularly digital ones, has an impact on all sectors. For example, thanks to industrial digitization, manufacturing is becoming smarter.

Artificial Intelligence drives innovation in the information and communications technology sector. It enhances the performance and efficiency of communication networks. Its potential to support these networks and communication services is enormous.

Data science continues to grow in scope, to the point where it now covers all human activities: transport, education, industry, healthcare, services, and so on. The harmonious combination of data science and Artificial Intelligence addresses the foundations of data management and analysis in all its forms (massive, complex, heterogeneous, uncertain...) and its concrete applications in major fields such as healthcare and cybersecurity.

Computer Vision is a computer science discipline which involves implementing a set of technologies that enable a computer to "see", and above all to understand its environment and draw conclusions from it. The tools and methods used may be hardware (cameras, imaging devices) or software (algorithms, etc.). They enable a computer to interpret a visual element. Synonyms for this discipline include Computer Vision, Computer Vision and Machine Vision. Computer vision, which focuses on machine-based image processing, is sometimes confused with machine vision, which is the science of making computers see. Machine vision captures and analyzes visual information using a camera, analog-to-digital conversion and digital signal processing. It is often compared to human eyesight, but machine vision is not linked to biology and can be programmed to see through walls, for example. It is used in a range of applications from signature identification to medical image analysis. Computer vision is important in the field of Artificial Intelligence. Improvements in the way machines observe and interpret the environments in which they find themselves could lead to technological developments that until now have been the stuff of science fiction films.

The term "virtual reality" (or immersive multimedia or computer-simulated reality or Virtual Reality) refers to devices that digitally simulate an environment by machine (computer). It's an immersive computer technology that simulates the physical presence of a user in an environment artificially generated by software. Depending on the technologies employed, it enables the user to experience a virtual universe through his or her various senses: most often sight, but also touch, hearing and smell. Virtual reality can be used to make abstract problems concrete, particularly in the field **of** Artificial Intelligence. Virtual reality and Artificial Intelligence make an effective pair. The 2020 World Conference on the Virtual Reality (VR) Industry will be held at the end of October 2020 in Nanchang, capital of Jiangxi province in eastern China. Co-organized by the Ministry of Industry and Information Technology (MIIT) and the Jiangxi provincial government, the conference is held annually in Nanchang. This year's two-day event will take place both online and offline this year, and participants will explore issues related to extended reality (XR), cloud VR, industrial ecology and entertainment gaming. During the 2019 conference, a total of 104 VR industry agreements and projects are signed. China is witnessing the maturation and expansion of the VR industry.

Augmented reality (or AR) is a technology that enables the integration of 2D or 3D virtual elements (in real time) within a real environment.

The principle is to combine the virtual and the real, and give the illusion of perfect integration to the user. The technology works via a terminal that films the real world and inlays live virtual objects, animations, text, data and sound, which the user views from the screen. This can be a smartphone, a touch-sensitive tablet, a pair of glasses, a headset or a head-up display system. By combining augmented reality and Artificial Intelligence, the virtual environment becomes not only more intelligent but also more personal. Experts predict that the convergence of augmented reality and Artificial Intelligence technologies will change the world.

Blockchain is a transparent, secure technological system for storing and transmitting information that operates without a central control body. In practice, exchange is peer-to-peer, without intermediaries; the register that lists all transactions enables traceability and record-keeping by all users; the constant verification of transactions is what we call a distributed consensus. Blockchain and Artificial Intelligence can work together to offer a wider range of applications. By combining the advantages of each technology, certain constraints can be circumvented. Blockchain and Artificial Intelligence can create a direct link between producers and consumers. Information is then stored, secured and used transparently. AI improves the quality of information transmitted and simplifies task execution, while blockchain provides visibility into the execution of Artificial Intelligence and enables information and connections to be secured.

Additive manufacturing" (AM), as opposed to subtractive manufacturing where material is removed to achieve the desired shape, is a term that encompasses many others, such as "3D printing", "rapid prototyping", "rapid manufacturing", "direct digital manufacturing" or "layer-by-layer manufacturing". In additive manufacturing, 3D parts are constructed by adding successive layers of material under computer control. The term 3D, meaning three dimensions, is used, among other things, for computer-generated images. The combination of Artificial Intelligence and 3D printing technologies can, among other things, increase the performance of a 3D printer, reducing the risk of error and facilitating automated production. More and more startups and research projects are integrating AI into 3D printing products and services.

g) **Contribution of Artificial Intelligence (AI) to scientific discovery:** exploring the potential of AI to accelerate the scientific discovery process and extract useful information from increasingly large datasets.

Artificial Intelligence is revolutionizing scientific and technological research. In most fields of scientific research, a large part of the work is done by Artificial Intelligence technologies. Artificial Intelligence is used to collect and process data on a massive scale, to reproduce and reduce the costs of experiments, and to accelerate scientific discovery.

Artificial Intelligence is becoming a crucial issue for governments, businesses, research bodies and other organizations. More and more scientific and technological research organizations are integrating data science and Artificial Intelligence to enable their researchers to push back the boundaries of science and deliver, among other things, life-saving medicines. These organizations optimize the time dedicated to discovery. Data science and AI help researchers to analyze and interpret data faster and more accurately. Artificial Intelligence is a key enabler of discovery, transforming the discovery process by rapidly generating innovative ideas, and developing and classifying these ideas using predictions based on the large datasets now available. For example, in the field of drug production, Artificial Intelligence has great potential for improving quality and reducing the time needed to discover a potential drug candidate with good medicinal properties. In various fields, Artificial Intelligence intensifies the pace of scientific discovery. It accelerates scientific production and the dissemination of knowledge.

In scientific research, AI is a source of innovation in all its forms, speeding up the process of scientific discovery and extracting useful information from increasingly voluminous data sets. While the technological innovation driven by AI is undoubtedly its most spectacular effect, it goes hand in hand with innovation in uses, services and products, economic models, marketing and sales models, organizational models, and social innovation. Artificial Intelligence is truly bringing about profound transformations in all these dimensions.

Artificial Intelligence can, among other things, recognize a cat, drive a car, paint new pictures, solve complex problems and help to advance many things, including scientific research. It can also make real discoveries; but it is not considered an inventor when filing for a patent. On April 27, 2020, the US Patent and Trademark Office ruled that inventors can only be natural persons, i.e. human beings. According to the US Patent and Trademark Office, the Dabus AI could not be considered an inventor, even though no human was involved in its inventions. The researcher, physicist Stephen Thaler, creator of the algorithm, felt that he could not be considered the author of the invention in question. In December 2019, the European Patent Office took a similar decision for the same reasons.

Artificial Intelligence could transform the way we conduct, structure and understand scientific research. This evolution will require scientists and engineers to acquire new skills to keep up to date.

It could lead to the supremacy of AI over research organized by and for humans.

h) **International cooperation at global and regional levels in the service of inclusive and trustworthy Artificial Intelligence, universal debate led on AI and international meetings dedicated to AI**

The world is in turmoil. A variety of social, economic and political changes, upheavals and disruptions are taking place on a massive scale, driven by a combination of digital transformation and globalization. Rapid technological advances in Artificial Intelligence (AI), along with other technological advances such as robotics, cloud computing and the Internet of Things, are transforming disciplines, economies and industries, and challenging what it means to be human. The impacts of AI affect all sectors of human society, from the political to the social, including education, ecology and the economy. It's worth noting that in May 1997, during the six-game rematch between man and machine, the whole planet could only witness the superiority of the computer and its "*intelligence*", which that day enabled it to beat the world champion and open up a world of limitless possibilities. Technology has continued to perfect itself ever since, and machines have become even more intelligent over the years. Artificial Intelligence is a fascinating and rapidly expanding field. New feats of AI technology are frequently reported in the press.

Over time, international cooperation in the field of Artificial Intelligence is developing to ensure, among other things, that the AI revolution does not widen the already considerable gaps between developed and developing countries, and within countries. Global, cross-sectoral, North-South and South-South cooperation and partnerships are crucial in this respect. The promise of Artificial Intelligence for All must enable everyone to benefit from the technological revolution underway, and to access its fruits, particularly in terms of innovation and knowledge.

As a global laboratory of ideas, a driving force in standard-setting, a supporter of policy formulation, and a developer of human and institutional capacities, UNESCO is called upon to play a key role in facilitating international cooperation and influencing the future transformations of human societies brought about by Artificial Intelligence. UNESCO's mandate implies a human-centered approach to AI. This UN organization is working i) to refocus dialogue to include the impact of AI on universal values, norms and internationally recognized standards, ii) to incorporate its role in combating inequalities in access to knowledge, research and the diversity of cultural expressions, iii) to ensure that AI does not widen the technological divide between and within countries.

UNESCO organizes the annual Mobile Learning Week, the United Nations' flagship event for information and communication technologies (ICT) in education. The 11ème edition of Mobile Learning Week took place from 05 to 08 March 2019 in Paris at UNESCO's main headquarters. The theme of this edition, which continued the debate on the role of AI in education, focused on the benefits and challenges following the use of Artificial Intelligence (AI) for sustainable development and more specifically in education, with a view to making it more inclusive and accessible to all. On the eve of the launch of the 11ème edition of Mobile Learning Week, UNESCO organized the high-level global conference "*Principles for AI: towards a humanistic approach?*" on March 04, 2019. On this occasion, UNESCO brought together stakeholders from the public and private sectors, the technical community, the media, academia, civil society and international organizations. The conference facilitated dialogue between stakeholders on the benefits and challenges of AI and its applications. The edition of Mobile Learning Week 2020, scheduled for March 02 to 06, 2020, has been postponed due to current concerns about the Covd-19 epidemic. It is planned that this 12ème edition will be reserved for in-depth analysis of both the risks and potential benefits of AI and inclusion in education. The three main themes of Mobile Learning Week 2020 will be: i) How to promote inclusive access to AI and new digital opportunities? ii) How to leverage AI and digital innovations to advance inclusion in education? iii) How to ensure non-discriminatory and gender-sensitive use of AI in education?

As part of its International Hydrological Program (IHP), UNESCO began developing Artificial Intelligence applications in 2005, in partnership with university teams, including one from the University of California at Irvine in the USA. The Global Water and Arid Zone Development Information (G-WADI) geoserver uses neural network algorithms to estimate rainfall worldwide in real time. The application is used to facilitate emergency planning and management of hydrological hazards such as floods, droughts and hurricanes. In addition, scientists working with UNESCO use a wide range of digital tools to analyze vast quantities of data in fields such as water management and climate change assessment. Thanks to the Internet of Things, they can also improve urban water management (smart water networks).

UNESCO is leading several AI programs. It has also contributed to the creation of the International Research Centre on Artificial Intelligence (IRCAI), as a UNESCO category 2 center in Ljubljana, Slovenia. The creation of the IRCAI was debated at the 206ème session of UNESCO's Executive Board, and subsequently approved at the 40ème session of UNESCO's General Conference. The latter validated the proposal and authorized the Director-General to sign an agreement between UNESCO and the

Slovenian Government concerning the creation and operation of the Centre. Due to the Covid-19 pandemic, the agreement was signed remotely, on March 05, 2020, by the Slovenian Minister of Education, Science and Sport and the Deputy Prime Minister, with UNESCO's Assistant Director-General for Communication and Information representing the Director-General. The International Research Center for Artificial Intelligence (IRCAI) has launched the Corona Virus Media Watch, which provides updates on global and national news based on a selection of media entities with open online information. The IRCAI will, among other things, maximize the benefits of AI for achieving the Sustainable Development Goals, and accelerate the establishment of a multi-stakeholder mechanism to test AI against ethical, legal, openness and policy challenges. The Center will also bring special attention and additional expertise to UNESCO's AI programs. In particular, it will harness the power and capabilities of AI in UNESCO's various fields of competence by producing relevant statistics on AI, AI-related applications and associated technological innovations. The creation of the center is also in line with a recent UNESCO publication entitled "Steering *AI* and *Advanced* ICTs for Knowledge Societies". This publication highlights some of the challenges and opportunities of AI from a human rights, openness, inclusive access and multi-stakeholder perspective. It advocates freedom from both technological utopia and dystopian thinking, while paying particular attention to the role of human agency and human-centered values in the development of AI.

The International Telecommunication Union (ITU), the United Nations' specialized agency for information and communication technologies, has organized the AI for Goud Global Summit annually since 2017. This Artificial Intelligence Global Summit is the United Nations' leading forum dedicated to Artificial Intelligence. The first edition triggered the first inclusive global dialogue on beneficial AI. It established the framework for a global dialogue on the prospects for using Artificial Intelligence in different fields for the common good. Following the success of this edition, the second edition is organized on May 15 and 17, 2018 in Geneva, in partnership with the XPRIZE Foundation, the Association for Computing Machinery (ACM) and several United Nations organizations. This action-oriented 2ème edition continued the dialogue by focusing on the implementation of certain solutions incorporating AI, with a view to long-term solutions, and therefore sustainable in every sense of the word. The 2018 summit focused on impactful AI solutions capable of generating long-term benefits and helping to achieve the SDGs. The second edition continued to formulate strategies aimed at both the reliable, safe and inclusive development of technologies using Artificial Intelligence and ensuring that everyone can enjoy equitable access to the benefits these technologies offer. The third edition of the Global Artificial Intelligence Summit, held from May 28 to 31, 2019 in Geneva, highlighted Artificial Intelligence projects in fields as diverse as education, healthcare and well-being, social and economic equality, space research and safe and intelligent mobility. Summit participants agreed that achieving global benefits would require the establishment of a common enabling infrastructure, known as the "*AI Commons*", to enable the sharing of knowledge, data, resources and solution-oriented approaches, with a view to encouraging the design and implementation of projects focused on Artificial Intelligence for Social Good. The fourth edition of the World Summit on Artificial Intelligence, scheduled for May 2020, will be held from September 21 to 25, 2020 in Geneva, due to the evolution of the Covid-19 disease pandemic. The AI for Good series is the UN's leading platform for inclusive international dialogue on AI, aiming to build a common understanding of the capabilities of emerging AI technologies. It identifies practical applications of AI to accelerate progress towards the Sustainable Development Goals (SDGs) and establishes collaboration to help these applications achieve global impact. ITU is well placed to guide AI innovation towards achieving the SDGs. In addition, following the success of the first AI for Good Global Summit, ITU has launched a global Artificial Intelligence repository to identify AI-related projects, research initiatives, think tanks and organizations that can accelerate progress towards the 17 SDGs.

The Organisation for Economic Co-operation and Development (OECD), which comprises the Directorate for Science, Technology and Innovation and the OECD Centre for Educational Research and Innovation (CERI), has created the OECD Artificial Intelligence Expert Group (AIGO or OECD Network of Experts **on** AI -ONE AI). This Network provides input from political, technical and business experts to inform OECD analysis and recommendations. It is a multi-disciplinary, multi-stakeholder group. The OECD's work focuses, among other things, on scientific and technological cooperation, including in the field of Artificial Intelligence. It organizes the Global Science Forum (formerly the MegaScience Forum). The OECD Forum is a forum for dialogue between senior science policy officials from its member countries. Its aim is to highlight and maximize opportunities for international cooperation in basic research. The Forum sets up ad hoc working groups and workshops to carry out technical analyses and draw up recommendations for governments. These groups bring together government representatives, scientific experts and representatives of international organizations. OECD committees have set up a number of Global Forums on various themes, including the Global Forum on Digital Security for Prosperity. OECD Global Forums address global issues. They help foster a convergence of views from a wide range of relevant actors on policy standards and best practices, not limited to committee members and partners, and highlight emerging issues. In a context marked by the transformation of the way public authorities, businesses and human societies operate by "*Blockchain*" (blockchain), massive data analysis, Artificial Intelligence and civic technology, the 7ème Annual OECD Forum on Integrity and the Fight against Corruption, held on March 20 and 21, 2019 at the OECD Conference Centre, examined the promises and risks of new technologies for integrity and the fight against corruption. Discussions included international corruption, illicit financial flows, responsible lobbying, golden visas as well as how social media influence elections.

At the annual Council Meeting at Ministerial Level, on the theme "*Digital transition for sustainable development: opportunities and challenges*", held on May 22 and 20, 2019 in Paris at the OECD Conference Centre, the 42 OECD member and partner countries officially adopted, on May 22, 2019, the first set of intergovernmental principles on Artificial Intelligence. The signatories commit to considering robustness, security, fairness, reliability and trust as international standards that they undertake to respect and promote. The OECD Principles on Artificial Intelligence were drawn up by a multidisciplinary group of over 50 experts from government, academia, business, civil society, international bodies, the technical community and trade unions. These value-based OECD Principles on Artificial Intelligence, for the responsible deployment of trustworthy AI, applicable within the framework of public policy and international cooperation, and relevant to companies and investors involved in the design, operation and financing of Artificial Intelligence systems, are:
i) serve the interests of individuals and the planet by promoting inclusive growth, sustainable development and well-being;
ii) respect the rule of law, human rights, democratic values and diversity, and be accompanied by appropriate safeguards - such as human intervention in case of need - in order to strive for a fair and equitable society;

iii) ensure transparency and responsible disclosure of information related to AI systems, so that people know when they are interacting with such systems and can challenge the results;

iv) ensure the robustness, reliability and safety of AI systems throughout their lifecycle, and the ongoing identification, assessment and control of related risks;

v) make organizations and individuals responsible for the development and operation of AI systems accountable for their proper functioning and compliance with the above principles.

The OECD Principles on Artificial Intelligence, like the rest of the OECD Guidelines, are an internationally recognized, legitimate and enforceable source of reference for defining, advancing and assessing the social responsibility of governments, companies and investors alike. The OECD Principles on Artificial Intelligence are supported by the European Commission. These principles complement the recommendations of the European Union's High Level Expert Group defining Ethical Guidelines for Trustworthy Artificial Intelligence. The responsible integration of Artificial Intelligence is now a component of corporate social responsibility .

The first meeting of the OECD Network of Experts on AI (ONE AI) was held in Paris on February 27 and 28, 2020. The OECD Artificial Intelligence Policy Observatory is launched on the first day of this meeting, at a joint session of ONE AI and the OECD Digital Steering Group. The Council of Europe has been invited to take part in the meeting, providing an opportunity to present the organization's activities in the field of Artificial Intelligence regulation, including the work of the Ad Hoc Committee (CAHAI).

The 64ème General Conference of the International Atomic Energy Agency (IAEA), the supreme governing body of this UN organization, was held from September 21 to 25, 2020 at the

Vienna International Center. This session was held against a difficult global backdrop and a particular international context due to the Covid-19 pandemic. This year marks a pivotal phase for the IAEA, which faces unprecedented challenges imposed by containment and changes to conventional ways of working as a result of the pandemic. The IAEA provides more than 125 countries around the world with the technical expertise and nuclear and radioactive equipment needed to detect the Covid-19 virus and contain its spread. This year sees the launch of the ZODIAC (integrated action against zoonoses) initiative, designed to reduce the intensity of potential future pandemics through the use of nuclear energy. During the Covid-19 pandemic, a third of African member states received substantial assistance in the form of nuclear technology equipment for the early detection and containment of Covid-19. Under the motto *"Atoms for Peace and Development"*, this session of the General Conference included 39 side events held online, some of which are also open to the public. Aimed at highlighting the work carried out at the IAEA and in Member States using nuclear techniques, these events included focuses on the possible applications of Artificial Intelligence-based approaches to nuclear science, the contribution of nuclear medicine to the treatment of cancer by radiotherapy, and the protection of the world's water resources from over-exploitation and contamination. On September 21, 2020 in Vienna, the Kingdom of Morocco was officially elected President of the 64ème IAEA General Conference, the governing body of this UN organization. This is the first time the Kingdom of Morocco has been unanimously acclaimed to this prestigious post.

In some countries, structures dedicated to Artificial Intelligence are working on international cooperation in the AI field. In Quebec, for example, there is the Observatoire international sur les impacts sociétaux de l'Intelligence Artificielle et du numérique (OBVIA) in Laval. This

Observatory is financially supported by the Fonds de recherche du Québec. Montreal is also home to an international center of expertise for the advancement of AI. In France, the Observatoire des impacts technologiques économiques et sociétaux de l'Intelligence Artificielle (OTESIA) will be created in November 2019. The Canadian Institute for Advanced Research (CIFAR), a Canada-based global charity bringing together brilliant minds to find answers to science's and Humanity's biggest questions, administered and organized, from June 2019 to June 2020 in Canada, France and the UK, in partnership with France's Centre national de la recherche scientifique (CNRS) and the UK's UK Research and Innovation (UKRI), a series of international research workshops as part of its Artificial Intelligence and Society program to examine the economic, ethical, political and legal implications of Artificial Intelligence on human societies. The interdisciplinary teams formed will examine the impact of AI on different groups of people and sectors of activity. This series of workshops is the second organized under the aegis of the Artificial Intelligence and Society program launched in 2017 by CIFAR. An important pillar of CIFAR's Pan-Canadian AI Strategy, this program enjoys a $125 million grant allocated by the Canadian Government to ensure Canada's leadership in machine learning research and education. In Morocco, the International Observatory on the Technological, Economic and Societal Impacts of Artificial Intelligence has been operating at the ISTIGOP Scientific Institute since its creation in 2012.

China makes Artificial Intelligence a field of cooperation with certain countries including France, the USA and Morocco. Sino-French cooperation in Artificial Intelligence formalized in early 2018. The 14ème session of the Sino-French Joint Scientific and Technological Commission, meeting on February 25, 2019 in Beijing, defined seven priority themes for scientific cooperation between France and China, including Artificial Intelligence. There are American and Chinese academics conducting joint research in Artificial Intelligence, but collaborations are coming under increasing scrutiny from Washington, against a backdrop of trade tensions and technological rivalry with Beijing. In China, the World Intelligence Congress (WIC), a major AI event, has been held annually since 2017, becoming a major event for academic exchanges, exhibitions, open innovation and deep cooperation in smart technologies. The 4ème World Intelligent Congress, themed "*New Intelligent Era: Innovation, Energization and Ecology*", an event originally scheduled for April 2020 and postponed due to the Covid-19 pandemic, was held online on June 23-24, 2020 in Tianjin, northern China. This Congress introduced a new conference model "*on the cloud*". In his keynote address, the vice-chairman of the National Committee of the Chinese People's Political Consultative Conference and president of the Chinese Association for Science and Technology declared that the success of this conference

"*establishes a superior platform for Artificial Intelligence exchanges. It is also an invitation to cooperation from all over the world, made by Chinese researchers and enterprises in the field of artificial intelligence. We will promote Big Data, use blockchain and innovate cloud services in epidemic prevention and control. We will develop new industries, promote intelligence and digitization throughout the industrial chain, and continuously work for the close integration of Artificial Intelligence and the real economy. We will create a new employment platform, an open source and sharing platform, and also promote the "Innovative China" brand. We will sustainably deepen basic research, build an artificial intelligence development platform and a world-class industrial system. We will deepen international cooperation in the field of artificial intelligence*".

With the "*four-in-one*" method, this grand gathering takes advantage of the means of "*conference, exhibition, competition + intelligent experience*".

According to China's People's Daily online, 58.6 million viewers watched the opening ceremony and themed summit on 40 live streaming sites and platforms, and the total number of views reached 392 million. Participants held a debate on, among other things, Artificial Intelligence to help control the global Covid-19 pandemic, contribute to the fight against poverty, promote sustainable development and develop a smart circular economy. Institutions presented reports, including the China Institute of Next-Generation Artificial Intelligence Development Strategies, which published the 2020 Report entitled "*The Development of China's Next-Generation Artificial Intelligence Technology Industry Facing New Challenges and Opportunities*". The topic of the closing ceremony of the 4ème World Intelligence Congress was "*AI and Love*".

Meanwhile, computer giant Microsoft has been conducting research into Artificial Intelligence, notably facial expression analysis, with Chinese academics affiliated to a military establishment - work that could be used for surveillance and censorship purposes. The emerging technology of Artificial Intelligence has become a major scientific and technological challenge. AI requires, among other things, a hybridization of knowledge and an assessment of its impact on human societies. Some universities (Harvard, Yale, Stanford...) have set up "*Internet and Human Society*" research centers.

Humanity is at the dawn of a new era. A dialogue on the development of Artificial Intelligence, particularly between AI leaders around the world, is strongly felt at global level, to, among other things, ensure the design of a framework anchored in international cooperation.

i) Governance of Artificial Intelligence and organization of a Global Partnership on AI

The potential of Artificial Intelligence extends to all areas of public service management, particularly administrative, business and human society. That's why it's crucial to pay the necessary attention to its governance. More generally, inclusive innovation requires inclusive, anticipatory governance of technological change, including impact assessment (benefits, costs, etc.) and active participation in future development.

Artificial Intelligence poses major governance challenges, including managerial, legal and ethical issues. Democratic principles and human rights must govern the implementation and use of Artificial Intelligence. A crucial question arises: who will govern AI, whose lifeblood is the Internet, to encourage innovation in the field of Artificial Intelligence, while reducing the risks as much as possible? The Internet is a major source of data, computing power and telecommunications infrastructure. All stakeholders - governments, intergovernmental organizations, businesses, academia and civil society - are increasingly impacted by AI. These multiple stakeholders have a strong interest in the evolution of, among other things, the standards, policies and codes that help govern Artificial Intelligence. It is worth noting that in the field of AI, policy-makers are torn between two things: on the one hand, they must establish the conditions that will enable AI to flourish and deliver benefits that will benefit everyone; on the other, they must be aware of and combat the harms that certain AI applications can generate and reinforce.

Artificial Intelligence governance issues are linked to those of Internet governance, which are dealt with at the Internet Governance Forum, created as the United Nations' open discussion platform on the main legal, political, social and technical issues relating to the Internet. The Internet is a gigantic global network, a network of networks, linking users from all horizons, regardless of national or geographical boundaries, and an extremely flexible platform for supporting a multitude of communication services. The Internet is omnipresent in the economy, politics, human society and culture of all nations. Having access to a secure and stable Internet connection is essential for reducing the digital divide and inequalities. The Internet can make a major contribution to strengthening human capital and opening up new opportunities. It has become inseparable from the advent of the information society. The question of its governance remains a global issue of great complexity. The first Global Forum on Internet Governance, held in Athens from October 30 to November 02, 2006, was convened by the UN Secretary-General at the request of participants at the second World Summit on the Information Society, held in Tunis in 2005, to promote the sustainability, stability, security and development of the Internet.

At the G7 Summit held on June 08 and 09, 2018 in Charlevoix, Quebec, one of the eight commitment statements issued by G7 leaders consists of the "*Charlevoix Shared Vision on the Future of Artificial Intelligence*". To realize the benefits of Artificial Intelligence, G7 leaders recognized.
"*that a human-centered approach to Artificial Intelligence has the power to provide us with new sources of economic growth, bring considerable benefits to our societies, and enable us to tackle some of our most pressing challenges.*"

Following the 2017 G7 ICT and Industry Ministers' meeting in Turin, Italy, at which they expressed a human-centric vision of AI focused on innovation and economic growth, and following the G7 Innovation Ministers' Statement on Artificial Intelligence made at the conclusion of the meeting held on March 28, 2018 in Montreal, Canada, aware of the need for international cooperation and coordination to harness the full potential of Artificial Intelligence and bring its benefits to all citizens,

Canada and France, which on June 07, 2018 expressed their desire to promote a human-centric vision of Artificial Intelligence, are working alongside the international community, particularly the other G7 members, to create an international panel of experts on Artificial Intelligence (G2IA or IPAI for international panel on artificial intelligence) -an Artificial Intelligence "IPCC"- with the mission of encouraging and guiding the responsible development of Artificial Intelligence based on human rights, inclusion, diversity, innovation and economic growth, and ensuring that this technology serves Humanity as a whole.

The G7 Innovation Ministers held a multi-stakeholder conference on Artificial Intelligence on December 06, 2018 in Montreal, Canada. The event brought together nearly 150 participants nominated by G7 partners, including several leading Artificial Intelligence experts from academia and research institutions, as well as civil society. The event was divided into four main working sessions: i) the societal challenges of Artificial Intelligence, ii) innovation in Artificial Intelligence, iii) trust in Artificial Intelligence, iv) the challenges of Artificial Intelligence for the labor market and skills. At the G7 multi-stakeholder conference on Artificial Intelligence, the Canadian Prime Minister and the French Minister announced the terms of reference for the International Artificial Intelligence Expert Group, the first step towards its creation.

One of the priorities of the French presidency of the G7 for the Biarritz Summit in 2019 is the fight against inequality through the development of digital technology and Artificial Intelligence. The informal meeting of G7 Digital Ministers, on the theme of "*Building Trusting Digital Together*", was held on May 15, 2019 in Paris. To ensure that this ministerial meeting is representative of the multiple realities of digital transformation and its cross-border nature, four major non-G7 democracies (India, Australia, New Zealand and Chile) as well as three international organizations (OECD, ITU and UNESCO) are invited to take part in this meeting and make the same commitments as G7 member states. With regard to the development of Artificial Intelligence technologies, the Ministers discussed how AI could contribute to the fight against inequalities, for example by taking account of inclusion issues in the selection of datasets and in the development of AI technologies, but also by designing innovative AI applications in areas linked to inclusion. They also recognized the need to strengthen international cooperation in AI to achieve these objectives. Ministers discussed the proposed International Expert Group on Artificial Intelligence. In the section on making platforms accountable in the fight against dangerous content on the Internet, the Ministers discussed the fight against dangerous content online, in particular by making online platforms accountable and transparent. They also discussed the *"smart regulation"* approach promoted by France in this area. Discussions also focused on the draft Charter for an Open, Free and Secure Internet. The G7 Leaders' Summit was held from August 24 to 26, 2019 in Biarritz, France. At this Summit, leaders discussed, among other things, the Global Partnership on Artificial Intelligence (GPIA). The International Expert Group on Artificial Intelligence was officially launched at this G7 Summit. It would comprise a steering committee and working groups, each focusing on a specific AI-related theme, such as AI governance, technological developments or impacts (on the future of work, for example), as well as a secretariat. The group would also organize a conference of international Artificial Intelligence experts once a year, entitled the *"Expert Group Multi-Stakeholder Plenary Assembly"*. It would bring together experts and stakeholders from all over the world, from the public and private sectors, from academia and research, and more broadly, from civil society.

France has organized the Global Forum on AI for Humanity (GFAIH) from October 28 to 30,

2019 in Paris, under the high patronage of the President of the Republic, with a view to preparing a Global Partnership on AI (GPAI or GPAI in English), as decided at the last G7 summit. Around 150 leading figures from the worlds of science, innovation and politics are present to discuss opportunities, problems and solutions on the theme of AI in workshops and plenary sessions. The Forum brought together experts in AI, social sciences, humanities and engineering, as well as innovators, economic players, policy-makers and representatives of civil society, to i) reach a common understanding of the opportunities brought by AI, the challenges to be met, and the methods and tools to address them, ii) deliberate on projects, studies and social experiments that can lead to a shared body of knowledge and shape R&D programs, iii) consider Global Partnership initiatives to put AI advances to work for Humanity. The Forum addressed the major issues associated with the development of Artificial Intelligence. Technology has revolutionized the way we live. But it also poses a number of challenges, such as the risks associated with data security, confidentiality and the impact of digital development. In his closing speech, the President of the French Republic was keen to support France's commitment and positioning in a technological move towards responsible Artificial Intelligence. The Forum served as an official springboard for the launch of the PMIA and set the agenda for future PMAI working groups.

The process of creating the secretariat of the Global Partnership on Artificial Intelligence (GPAI or Gee-Pay) at the OECD is, as of mid-June 2020, in its final phase. The secretariat is being set up within the OECD, which is a permanent observer. On June 15, 2020, Canada and France, together with Australia, the European Union, Germany, Italy, India, Japan, the Republic of Korea, Mexico, New Zealand, Singapore, Slovenia, the United Kingdom and the United States of America, launched the Global Partnership on Artificial Intelligence, which

would encourage and guide the responsible development of Artificial Intelligence based on human rights, inclusion, diversity, innovation and economic growth. The Global Partnership on Artificial Intelligence initially consists of 4 dedicated working groups:
- to responsible AI;
- data governance;
- to the future of work;
- innovation & marketing.

Two centers of expertise, one in Montreal and the other in Paris, would support the partnership. The Paris center of expertise would be provided by INRIA, and would provide administrative and research support. As part of a first virtual mission to Paris on June 25, 2020, due to the Covid-19 pandemic, Canadian and French ministers met to take stock of the work undertaken by Quebec and France in the digital field, and more specifically in Artificial Intelligence. They welcomed the launch of the Montreal International Centre of Expertise in Artificial Intelligence (MIACE), and reiterated their desire to contribute, with the PMIA's founding partners, to the responsible development and human-centered use of Artificial Intelligence (AI), while respecting human rights, fundamental freedoms and their shared democratic values.

To encourage a dialogue on the development of human-centered Artificial Intelligence, UNESCO organized the high-level Global Conference *"Principles for AI: towards a humanistic approach?"* on March 04, 2019 in Paris at its headquarters. UNESCO brought together stakeholders from the public and private sectors, the technical community, academia, civil society, international organizations and the media. At the conference, UNESCO's Director-General called for human-centered governance of Artificial Intelligence. She stressed the imperative of
"define a set of ethical principles to guide this technological disruption. So that it serves collective preferences. So that it is based on humanist values".

Referring to UNESCO's work on AI, the Director-General of UNESCO announced that the Organization would be able to work on the basis of a first report by the World Commission on the Ethics of Scientific Knowledge and Technology (COMEST). The Secretary-General of the Organisation for Economic Co-operation and Development (OECD) reiterated the importance of cooperation to ensure that AI becomes an engine for inclusive and sustainable growth. He said, *"We have no room for error, because while AI fuels optimism, it is also a source of anxiety and ethical concerns."* He stressed the need to work with UNESCO in a concerted effort to *"make AI less artificial and more intelligent"*. This high-level Global Conference on Artificial Intelligence facilitated dialogue between AI leaders from around the world and on ways to ensure the design of human-centered and ethical principles for AI and a framework rooted in international cooperation. It facilitated dialogue between stakeholders on the benefits and challenges associated with AI and its applications. Participants at this UNESCO World Conference emphasized the need to ensure rights-based, human-centered governance of AI. In addition, this UNESCO World Conference also launched Mobile Learning Week, the United Nations' flagship conference on new technologies for education, held from 05 to 08 March 2019 on the theme *"Artificial Intelligence for Sustainable Development"*. It should be noted that the High-Level Global Conference on Artificial Intelligence was part of a series of events organized by UNESCO on AI. It followed the debate organized at headquarters on January 22, 2019 on the ethics of new technologies and Artificial Intelligence *"The high-tech future for man: hope or fear?"*, in a context marked by rapid advances in Artificial Intelligence and other cutting-edge technologies, including robotics, cloud computing and the Internet of Things, which are transforming disciplines, economies and industries, and challenging traditional ideas about what it means to be human, and at the Forum on Artificial

Intelligence in Africa organized, on December 12 and 13, 2018 in Benguérir, Morocco (see below). In addition, UNESCO has organized, from May 16 to 18, 2019 in Beijing, in partnership with the Chinese Government, a major conference on Artificial Intelligence and Education, the aim of which is to study new AI technologies and innovative practices in the use of AI in education.

Ahead of the 14ème edition of the Internet Governance Forum in Berlin, France hosted an international conference entitled "*Global Forum on AI for Humanity*" (GFAIH) in Paris on October 29 and 30, 2019. The aim of this event was to reflect on priority themes that could feed into the initial work of the international group of experts on Artificial Intelligence.

The fourteenth annual meeting of the Global Forum on Internet Governance, on the theme "*One world. One network. One Vision*", is hosted by the German Government from November 25 to 29, 2019 in Berlin. The sub-themes of the Internet Governance Forum in Berlin, opened by the UN Secretary-General and the German Federal Chancellor, are data governance, digital inclusion and security, stability and resilience. In his address, the UN Secretary-General noted, among other things, that whole swathes of the world's population are deprived of access to the Internet, and that Artificial Intelligence algorithms are helping to lock users into filter bubbles. He warned that the universality of the Internet is threatened by a triple digital, social and political divide. In her address, the German Chancellor pointed out that "it is increasingly *important to discuss together to shape the future of the Internet*", warning against the dangers of a "*fragmented Internet*". At the Forum, on November 27, 2019, UNESCO launched a publication entitled "*Piloting AI and advanced ICT for knowledge societies: a perspective based on Human Rights, Openness, Accessibility and Multi-stakeholder participation*", as part of an Open Forum entitled "*Formulating strategic options for the development of Big Data and AI'*. This UNESCO publication recognizes AI as an opportunity to achieve the United Nations Sustainable Development Goals (SDGs), through its contribution to building inclusive knowledge societies. It is part of the evaluation of AI through UNESCO's ROAM framework for Internet universality. There are also regional initiatives on the Internet Governance Forum. These include the annual African Internet Governance Forum (AfIGF). The 8ème edition of this Forum was held from September 10 to 12, 2019 in N'Djamena, Chad. In addition, there is the multi-stakeholder advisory group of the North African Internet Governance Forum (NAIGF). The 3ème annual meeting of this group was held on September 26 and 27, 2019 in Rabat. The meeting brought together several experts from the region representing different multi-stakeholder groups concerned with Internet governance issues in the region (Algeria, Egypt, Libya, Mauritania, Morocco, Sudan and Tunisia).

j) Robotic technologies, drones, AI-enabled autonomous vehicles AI-enabled autonomous vehicles and the emergence of Artificial Intelligence virtual idols in the cultural field

Robotics is, broadly speaking, all the scientific and industrial fields involved in the design and production of robots. It's the set of techniques **used to** automate certain tasks. Robotics technology has evolved from the first automata to animats and humanoids. Technical advances in digital and mechanical engineering have enabled the creation of increasingly sophisticated objects, capable of responding to a wide range of needs and carrying out increasingly complex tasks autonomously. Man often draws inspiration from nature to bring robots to life. Robotics combines four disciplines: mechanics, electronics, computer science and mathematics (robot intelligence). Robotics includes both physical robots executing pre-programmed actions (industrial robots on assembly lines), intelligent robots, and everything at the intersection of the two. There are, for example, assistant robots, such as those used to assist frail, dependent people, and *cobot* robots, which work alongside humans in the workshop or on the construction site. Robotics can be found in many sectors. Robots are increasingly powerful, useful and capable of holding a real conversation. Intelligent robots are making their appearance in the home. Drones, autonomous cars and super-powered mini-robots are emerging. Intelligent robotics is a form of Artificial Intelligence. Robots are objects, and as such devoid of affect, unlike human beings and animals. But modern robots have developed affective capacities that enable them to simulate emotions. Robots are an intellectual revolution for mankind. It should be pointed out that the word "*robot*" does not mean the same thing in Japan as it does in France. In Japan, a robot is a machine that performs relatively simple tasks. Perhaps Japanese industry is also different.

Robots first appeared in industry, originally in the automotive sector, in the 1960s. Factories are the ideal setting for robotization, since large-scale, standardized production runs provide the ideal framework for automation. For decades, industrial robots have been large, expensive and operated from static stations on the shop floor, performing a limited number of repetitive and sometimes dangerous tasks, such as welding and machining. With advances in technology, particularly digital technology, successive new generations of robots are being used. Industrial robotics can be deployed without direct interaction with humans. It has evolved, but its foundation remains the repetition of gestures and the standardization of tasks. Less bulky and more expensive, more autonomous, flexible and cooperative, they are programmable and can be used by workers with no particular qualifications. Some factories operate without people on the production lines (or only with supervisory staff). The first fully robotized industrial unit manufacturing cell phone screens for the RBD company opened in Dongguan, China, in 2015. In addition to improving process reliability, robots help to reduce lead times for the manufacture of finished products, and thus increase responsiveness to variations in retail demand. In developed countries, industrial employment has been drastically reduced by the introduction of industrial robots in factories. At every stage of technical progress, the question of the impact of these technologies on employment is raised. The effects are massive. Robotic technologies are beginning to make their appearance in modern agriculture. Robots are also increasingly playing new roles in the service sector: healthcare, education, training, business information, services for the elderly, security, etc. Sophia, a humanoid robot developed by Hanson Robotics, gave its first TV interview to CNBC's Andrew Ross Sorkin at the Future Investment Initiative in Saudi Arabia in October 2017. On this occasion, the host country even awarded him Saudi citizenship. In developed countries and certain Asian countries (China, Korea...), it's commonplace to come across robots that are actually operational on the street, at the shopping mall, railway station, airport or any other place frequently visited by the public. The market for personal and domestic service robots is growing year on year. The world of robots is undergoing spectacular technological advances, making solutions technically possible that only a few decades ago were the stuff of science fiction. The use of robots in a wide range of sectors is becoming a topic of public debate, with the idea that these losses are affecting the least qualified jobs, condemning many people to technological unemployment.

China National Offshore Oil Group Co., Ltd. ("CNOOC") announced, On September 20, 2020, that the first self-sustaining deepwater oil field cluster, Liuhua 16-2, has been successfully commissioned after 30 months of construction. To achieve this success, CNOOC overcame many world-class problems in the process of its completion and operation, and achieved many "firsts" in China, further improving the engineering technology system of deepwater oil and gas development with independent Chinese intellectual property rights and injecting new power into the protection of national energy security. The subsea production system of the Liuhua 16-2 oil group mainly comprises 26 subsea extraction trees, production manifolds, subsea cables, umbilicals and remote control systems, subsea pipelines and flexible risers. Most of these subsea production facilities were used for the first time in China.

In China, mining robots designed by Yuexin Intelligence are capable of handling the entire process of drilling, shoveling, loading and transporting ore. 5G technology is used for the first time in China's mining industry.

Smarter, more autonomous robots are emerging, thanks in part to improvements in a number of areas: computing performance, electromechanical design tools and numerically controlled machines, electrical energy storage and the energy efficiency of power electronics, the availability and performance of local digital (wireless) communications, the scale and performance of the Internet, and data storage capacities and computing power. Thanks to deep learning, robotics has undergone a veritable revolution in recent years. The more Artificial Intelligence improves, the more it provides relevant answers thanks to deep learning. But the challenges of robotics remain, particularly in the fields of perception, recognition of specific objects in cluttered environments, manipulation and cognition. *Industry 4.0*' unveils a different world of work. And in this new world, smart factories will function thanks to the empowerment of machines (see below).

Intelligent robots incorporate three main features: i) sensors to understand the environment, ii) processors to analyze it and make appropriate decisions, iii) actuators (motors, tools, articulated arms) to act on the real world. There are two parts to intelligent robot design: design of the physical robot and design of the autonomous decision-making part, the robot's intelligence. When it comes to getting the robot to interact with humans, the host function seems the most appropriate. A number of companies have developed robots with screens and, above all, Artificial Intelligence, enabling them to converse verbally with humans. Like many other scientific fields, robotics borrows its words from other fields, particularly those of cognition and human intelligence. Its action verbs are unambiguous: the robot picks up an object, walks, paints, welds and so on. Its disposition verbs (to be autonomous, to decide, etc.) confront people with risk. Among the institutions dedicated to Artificial Intelligence research is a laboratory for cognitive and interactive robotics. Cognition and robot interaction with humans are two important aspects.

The security and defense sectors are seeing major innovations in the form of intelligent robots and advances in Artificial Intelligence. Facial recognition, for example, has spread rapidly (see below).

The fantastic new developments in robotics are fascinating. French start-up Exotec has made a name for itself in logistics with its compact Skypod robots, capable of three-dimensional movement and designed to carry small, fast-moving loads. These logistics robots demonstrate the need for supply chain automation and digitalization solutions, both to ensure the continuity of the logistics chain and to guarantee the safety of particularly exposed personnel. French company Clinatec has developed an exoskeleton for paraplegics. Researchers at Stanford University have developed an ankle exoskeleton designed to facilitate running. It reduces the effort required and even allows you to run a little faster. Researchers at the University of Michigan have developed a new technique that gives amputees greater control over their neuroprostheses. They have coated the peripheral nerves, often damaged by amputation, with a muscle graft to amplify their electrical signal. The Spot robot-dog, a dog-like quadruped marketed by Boston Dynamics, has been used by the Massachusetts police since November 2019. This robot is making its debut on construction sites in Canada, and is used to access confined and dangerous areas. Since January 31, 2020, the quadruped has been present at Place Ville Marie, on a building complex in downtown Montreal, where it takes photos of different parts of the construction site using specialized software and a 360-degree camera attached to its back. According to press reports, since May 08, 2020, the Singapore Government has been using the Spot robot-dog to patrol Bishan-Ang Mo Kio Park. This robot-dog is equipped with cameras and managed remotely. Its role is to warn off walkers who fail to respect safe distances. The robot-dog calls out: *"For your safety and that of those around you, please keep a distance of one meter"*. Thanks to its cameras, the robot will also be able to estimate the number of visitors to parks, with fewer staff required. The Singaporean government is also using the Spot robot to deliver medication to Covid-19 sufferers confined to the Changi Exhibition Centre. As part of the fight against the Covid-19 viral pandemic, Rwanda acquired five intelligent anti-epidemic robots to screen for the new coronavirus on May 19, 2020, with the help of the UNDP - a first of its kind for the UNDP. These humanoids, manufactured by Zorabots, a Belgium-based technology company, and each bearing a Rwandan name, can also warn if someone is not wearing or is wearing their mask incorrectly, and digitally record patient data. To speed up coronavirus testing, a member of the Chinese Academy of Engineering announced at the end of May 2020 that a modified vehicle-mounted coronavirus detection laboratory is due to enter service in July 2020; it will speed up testing and avoid the possible infections of manual sampling. This is thanks to a new chip and a robot that can collect samples using buccal and nasal swabs. The Reuters news agency reported on May 25, 2020, that in South Korea, as part of the fight against the Covid-19 pandemic, the manager of a coffee shop in Daejeon is using a robot to respect social distancing. The coffee machine is integrated into this mobile robot, which prepares over 60 types of hot beverage. The robot moves around the café, takes orders from the people seated at the table, prepares the hot drinks and then brings them to the customers. The robot is also programmed to give users information on the best way to enjoy their drink, and to exchange data with other devices. It is also equipped with a program that calculates the best route to take from one point of the café to another. The use of this mobile robot reduces the risk of Covid-19 spreading, since only one human employee is needed to run the service. This employee takes care of the pastries and makes sure that the robot's built-in coffee machine doesn't run out of any ingredients. He's also in charge of cleaning. The robot, a multifunctional mechanical employee, was developed by Vision Semicon and a public scientific institute. In addition, according to an article published in Les Inrockuptibles magazine on June 25, 2020, Erica, a robot with Artificial Intelligence designed by Japanese scientists, has been chosen to star in a science-fiction film called b. In a first for the film industry, the lead role in a $70 million sci-fi movie has been given to a female Artificial Intelligence. Nasa launched its Perseverance Mars rover on July 17, 2020. This robot will collect geological data to improve our knowledge of the Martian soil.

Autonomous vehicles are equipped with an autopilot system that enables them to drive without human intervention in real traffic conditions. Progress in autonomous driving and navigation is fuelled, among other things, by advances in

Artificial Intelligence. All the information provided by the vehicle's equipment is processed by an Artificial Intelligence program, which decides which maneuvers to carry out by acting on servo-controls controlling the vehicle's main functions. Autonomous vehicles include drones, autonomous cars, self-driving buses and autonomous ships. In China, a first 4.4 km long 5G demonstration road for autonomous cars and buses went into service on September 03, 2020, in the Chinese province of Anhui. Thanks to the rapid information transfer of the 5G network, autonomous cars and buses are able to detect traffic lights, pedestrians and obstacles quickly and accurately. This demonstration route is open to all vehicles, autonomous or ordinary.

Drones are unmanned aircraft generally operated remotely from the ground. The unmanned aircraft system comprises an unmanned aerial vehicle, a ground controller and a communication system between the two. Drones can be programmed to fly autonomously or via wifi via a smartphone or tablet. There are different categories of drone use. These include unmanned drones capable of taking off from an aircraft carrier, landing on it and refueling in flight, all autonomously, unmanned ships capable of autonomous navigation in compliance with maritime law and conventions.

According to the Chinese press on June 16, 2020, featuring photos, Chinese scientists from Tsinghua University have developed an intelligent, autonomous air-ground vehicle. This electric drone, which can switch between a ground and a flight mode, can be used for deliveries and rescue missions. It has a four-wheel drive system and is equipped with a rotor to enable flight. The drone is capable of three-dimensional trajectory planning, and can perform vertical take-off and landing, land-use planning, hovering in the air and obstacle avoidance in flight. With its real-time perception module, the drone can recognize different types of obstacle or terrain. When it encounters obstacles or terrain that cannot be avoided on the ground, it can then switch to flight mode and search for an area more suitable for driving on the ground. This smooth, efficient changeover of working modes will help to improve transport efficiency. The vehicle is being tested in both urban and mountain environments, using complex terrain.

In the cultural sphere, some countries have launched virtual idols with Artificial Intelligence. We are witnessing the emergence of virtual idols, supported by the younger generation. The virtual idol trend originated in Japan, where the intellectual property industry has flourished. A Chinese virtual idol, Ling, made her global online debut on May 18, 2020, leading the latest Chinese Internet trend among positive influencers and cultural inheritors, and showcasing China's soft power and culture. Technology companies, relying on Artificial Intelligence, have opened up the process of intelligent characterization from intelligent modeling to Artificial Intelligence performance animation technology that stimulates facial expressions, eyes, body and finger movements. They generate short videos or real-time broadcasts for interaction and marketing of virtual intelligent property.

There is a huge demand for robots, especially service robots, as well as an increasingly widespread application of special robots. Robots are ideal for replacing humans in rescue work in dangerous situations. A report, released on August 20, 2019 by the China Institute of Electronics (CIE) at the World Robot Conference (WRC 2019) estimated that the global robotics market value could reach $29.41 billion in 2019 with a CAGR of 12.3% between 2014 and 2019. According to the report, the Chinese robotics market is growing strongly. During the Covid-19 epidemic, China's drone industry experienced accelerated development, with drones being used as essential tools to provide medical resources and spray disinfectants in China's villages. According to experts, China is currently seeking to play a dominant role in the global unmanned aircraft systems sector after recently launching its first international standard for the sector. The new China-led standard focused on the categorization and classification of civil unmanned aircraft systems, which form the basis of safe operating protocols for the drone industry. According to data from International Data Corp, China is currently the leader in civil drones, with DJI, a leading manufacturer, controlling over 70% of the sector worldwide.

The marketing of a robot is subject to strict standards defined by machine directives, which define the conditions of use to meet safety requirements. These directives are imposed right from the design stage, and define the environment in which the machine is to operate. For example, industrial robots used in the automotive industry are confined to areas where humans cannot enter.

Research is being carried out on, among other things, the robot of the future that will work alongside humans. This leads robotics researchers to develop an open sensitivity to the human model. The robot must do its job, be useful and efficient, but it must also be relevant and accepted in its behavior by humans. In the context of social robotics, future humanoid robots will be able to "*feel*" emotions and interact emotionally with human beings.

The development of robotics poses a number of challenges. Advances in robotization raise many questions, from the risk of automating jobs to interference in other aspects of everyday life. Are or will robots be able to replace people? For which tasks? What decisions does the robot have to make? In what situation? For what purpose? Will Artificial Intelligence surpass human intelligence? These are all legitimate questions that require dialogue. In education, robotic application scenarios are intriguing, ranging from teaching objects for an intuitive introduction to computer programming, to solutions for remote access or teacher assistance. The *"robot revolution" has been* making a lot of noise over the last two decades, particularly in the press. Beyond the quantitative aspects, the arrival of intelligent robots is profoundly transforming the relationship between man and machine, and changing work collectives. Skill requirements are changing rapidly, posing an unprecedented challenge to initial and continuing training systems.

k) Artificial Intelligence, the Internet of Things and Industry 4.0

The pace of innovation is phenomenal. They have led to the creation of the Internet of Things (IoT), whose definition cuts across conceptual and technical dimensions. This definition is not set in stone. According to the International Telecommunication Union, the Internet of Things is a

"global infrastructure for the information society, enabling advanced services by interconnecting objects (physical *or virtual) using existing or evolving interoperable information and communication technologies".*

The Internet of Things is characterized by connected physical objects with their own digital identity, capable of communicating with each other. At the heart of the Internet of Things lies an object's ability to interconnect and interact with its physical environment. It encompasses:

- objects connected directly to the Internet;
- machine-to-machine -M2M- i.e. machine-to-machine communication and access to information systems without human intervention, using Bluetooth, RFID, Wifi, 4G and 5G;
- *smart connected devices*" such as tablets and smartphones.

IoT is the direct, standardized digital identification (IP address, smtp, http protocols, etc.) of a physical object using a wireless communication system. It is closely linked to connected objects, to each other and to the network. Connected objects capture, store and retransmit data without requiring any human-to-human interaction. They have the ability to capture data and send it, via the Internet or other technologies. They interact with their environment via sensors. Thanks to its sensors, the connected object collects data relating to a target environment. In the field of the environment, this may involve sensors monitoring air quality, temperature, noise levels, the condition of a building, and so on. In logistics, sensors can be used to track goods for inventory management and routing. The connected object is integrated into an automated or non-automated process, and has the ability to receive and transmit orders to another macro-task. It interacts with the user, for real-time monitoring of information or remote control. The network creates a kind of bridge between the physical and virtual worlds. In the Internet of Things, an object can be a vehicle, an industrial machine or a parking space. In home automation, IoT covers all communicating household appliances, sensors (thermostats, smoke detectors, presence detectors, etc.), smart meters and security systems connected to devices such as home automation boxes. Connected objects are gradually being deployed in all sectors of the economy.

The Internet of Things (IoT) is increasingly penetrating people's daily lives. It is taking root in virtually every sector of activity, opening up a host of new opportunities, but also new security threats. The Internet of Things connects billions of objects and billions of people. It is considered one of the most powerful tools for creating, modifying and sharing an incalculable amount of information. Indeed, the IoT aims to make objects interact with each other and with people. It promises to drive major transformations in people's lives, democratizing new uses and services in the mobility sector. And yet, IoT experts estimate that only 1% of its potential is currently being exploited. That's why it's being compared to the Internet of the future.

The potential of the Internet of Things is realized through Artificial Intelligence. The InO has paved the way for countless innovations. Artificial Intelligence of Things (AIoT) combines Artificial Intelligence technologies with the infrastructure of the Internet of Things. AIoT combines AI technologies (machine learning, automatic natural language processing, speech recognition, image analysis) with data from connected sensors, systems or products to make operational decisions. AIoT transforms an ocean of data into a world of intelligence. As a result, connected objects operate more efficiently, human-machine interactions are improved, and data management and analytics are more advanced.

The Internet of Things and Artificial Intelligence are two particularly complementary technologies. AI makes the IoT smarter. Connected objects generate vast quantities of data, which must be stored and processed within the framework of Big DData. Big Data refers to data sets that have become so voluminous that they overwhelm human intuition and analysis capabilities, and even those of conventional database or information management tools. Machine learning then uses these immense oceans of data to improve processes and increase the autonomy of systems. Data lies at the heart of the link between IoT and AI. The notions of Internet of Things, Cloud and Big Data are complementary. The Cloud consists in harnessing the computing or storage power of remote computer servers via a network, usually the Internet. In the connected world, the Internet of Things is the data capture, Big Data is the fuel and AI is the brain.

The combination of AI and IoT makes it possible to boost productivity and increase automation within companies and organizations, while reducing costs. Many sectors are being transformed by this technological synergy, including the energy and logistics industries. The IoT phenomenon is also highly visible in the field of health and well-being, with the development of connected watches, connected bracelets and other sensors monitoring vital vitals. According to various projections, the number of connected objects is set to increase significantly over the coming years. In industry, the IoT concept refers to the integration of communicating objects into industrial systems to enhance performance, safety and security. Plants anticipate breakdowns before they happen, reduce unplanned downtime, and improve the safety of workers and citizens thanks to constant monitoring and faster response times. Artificial Intelligence enhances security around connected objects. The proliferation of terminals and sensors is accompanied by a severe downside: cyber-attacks. The race for innovation tends to leave security behind. As a result, connected objects are by nature a perfect target for cybercriminals, who use them as a gateway to access the network connected to them and steal all the data stored on them. Households equipped with connected objects are more vulnerable, as a home network does not have the sophisticated firewalls and intrusion detection systems that businesses have, and consumers are not yet vigilant enough to, among other things, change the default passwords on their devices themselves. Given the increase in the diversity of threats and the complexity of securing smart objects, Artificial Intelligence is the preferred solution. Complementing human supervision. In general, connected objects are a source of concern in terms of cybersecurity. Internet of Things security is still limited. There are companies specialized in IT security that can secure objects, emails, the Cloud, apps and nomadic corporate tools upstream and at the heart of the network. These advanced detection solutions are highly effective in preventing, countering and, where necessary, managing threats and attacks.

On May 12, 2019, China sent two satellites into orbit, Xingyun-2 01 and 02, to test space-based Internet of Things (IoT) and laser intersatellite communications technologies and a low-cost commercial satellite platform. It sent two satellites into space on May 31, 2020, which are placed in orbit. One of these satellites, HEAD-4, can collect information from orbit, including information on ships and aircraft, as well as the Internet of Things. Thanks to AI applications, this satellite can serve, among others, projects along the "*Belt and Road*". According to information from the China Aerospace Science and Industry Corporation, reproduced in the Chinese People's Daily online in French on June 12, 2020, China's IoT satellites, Xingyun-2 01 and 02, have completed Phase 1 in-orbit testing. These Xingyun-2 01 and 02 satellites use inter-satellite laser link technology, enabling the orbiting satellites to communicate over long distances and thus improve the real-time performance of communication services. The project is expected to solve problems detected in the communications grey zone of IoT companies, due to insufficient coverage of wireless cellular communications networks. Satellite Internet has become a buzzword in several major Chinese cities, such as Beijing, Shanghai and Chongqing, which have incorporated its development into their development programs as a priority. The "*Research White Paper on the Development of the Internet of Things in China's New Infrastructure*" has recently been published.

For the smart connected car industry, safety is a general concern of both the industry and the public. A side event to the 4ème World Intelligence Congress, held on June 23-24, 2020 in Tianjin's Xiqing District, the "International Forum on Innovation and Pilot Application Development for the Internet of Vehicles", themed "*Intelligent Internet of Vehicles, Leading a Better Life*", is being held on June 24, 2020. The event invited top Chinese and foreign experts, academics and industry leaders to discuss the current state and future of intelligent connected vehicles. At the forum, the deputy general manager of China Information and Communication Technologies Group Co emphasized that Internet of Vehicles technology and sensor technology complement each other. This makes it possible to form a technical framework of "*putting intelligence + networking*", to break the limits of individual vehicle intelligence and realize the interconnection of the global road network and participants, to ultimately form an important path for the development of autonomous driving. In recent years, the development of Internet of Vehicles technology has opened up more possibilities. The 2020 edition of the World Artificial Intelligence Conference (WAIC), on the theme of "*Intelligent Connectivity and Indivisible Community*", organized by Shangha City Hall in China, was held online from July 09 to 11, 2020, with meeting rooms arranged in Shanghai, the USA, Germany, France and Singapore. Free-access online exhibitions are also organized on this occasion, among others, with the virtual site of the 5G Global Innovation Port offering a panoramic view of the site located in the heart of Shanghai's Beiwaitan business zone.

Artificial Intelligence and the Internet of Things are symbiotic technologies united by a bond that will grow stronger over the coming years.

InO security is paramount, with every "*node*" ideally protected against spyware, malware and privacy-threatening intrusions. We also need to capitalize on the potential of the Internet of Things (IoT), a technology that holds great promise for the future.

The Industrial Internet, also known as the Industrial Internet of Things, is a key sector for the construction of new infrastructures. The term refers to the wider adoption of advanced technologies such as next-generation wireless networks, megadata, Artificial Intelligence and the Internet of Things. The Industrial Internet is not just an instrument, but also an ecosystem that links all elements of the industrial economy, including the industrial chain, the value chain, research and development, procurement, production and consumption. In China, the International Services Trade Fair 2020, with the theme "Global Services, Shared Prosperity", held from September 04 to 09, 2020, is marked by the International Services Trade Summit, four summit forums and over 100 additional industry seminars and forums. The show is the first major international economic and trade event organized online and offline by China since the start of the Covid-19 epidemic. The show highlighted new business models and forms, including digital commerce, 5G communications, industrial Internet, smart office and blockchain innovation, among others. The Committee for the Promotion of the Industrial Internet is being launched, on September 06, 2020 in Beijing, at the China 2020 International Service Trade Fair. It will focus on strategic research, the standards system, industrial solutions and other key areas of the Industrial Internet, as part of efforts to build a solid foundation for the consistent and healthy development of the sector in China. It will also promote innovations in areas such as workplace safety, energy, coal production, medical care, construction, automobiles and satellites, and strengthen the collection, sharing and exploration of the megadata value of the Industrial Internet.

At the Global Industrial Internet 2020 Conference, held on September 20-21, 2020 in Qingdao, Shandong province (eastern China), the deputy director of information and telecommunications at China's Ministry of Industry and Information Technology said on September 20, 2020, that China's industrial Internet sector has entered the fast lane. A large number of new breakthroughs, new models and new applications have emerged. China is adopting a new growth dynamic in the industrial Internet, as the country strives to become a bridgehead in the next generation of industrial development on a global scale. China has already developed over 70 regionally-influenced industrial Internet platforms with related applications covering more than 30 key industries across the country. In addition, over 350,000 industrial enterprises are connected to cloud platforms. Such advances are in line with Chinese President Xi Jinping's call to strengthen the innovation capacity of the industrial Internet and advance the integration between industrialization and computerization. China is betting big on the Industrial Internet of Things to boost productivity and improve efficiency by streamlining and automating manufacturing processes via Internet connectivity. It has called for the development of new infrastructures, including 5G, Artificial Intelligence and the Industrial Internet to offset the economic impact of the pandemic and stimulate sustainable growth. China's Industrial Internet opens up new opportunities for growth in the midst of the global industrial revolution. It has a potential beyond imagination, which not only promotes the modernization of manufacturing industry, but also determines China's ability to lead the next technology cycle. According to the CTO of the Global System for Mobile Communications Association (GSMA), China, backed by positive government support, is poised to dominate the global industrial Internet of Things market. There will be 13.8 billion such connections worldwide by 2025, and China will account for around 4.1 billion of them - a third of the global market.

Industry 4.0, also known as the fourth industrial revolution or factory of the future, is fundamentally characterized by intelligent automation and the integration of new technologies into the manufacturing company's value chain. It is a digital transformation that disrupts the enterprise, bringing radical changes to systems and processes, as well as to the workforce, management modes and business models. A key component of Industry 4.0 is the connectivity of data and objects. One of its pillars is digital continuity, i.e. the ability to have access to all information on a product throughout its lifecycle, **with a** view to, among other things, gaining exhaustive knowledge of the product from its concept phase right through to maintenance on the customer's premises, improving efficiency, achieving better quality and developing new products and functionalities more rapidly.

In several developed countries and some emerging countries (China..), more and more companies have decided to move to Industry 4.0.

I) Artificial intelligence and cloud computing

In the field of information and communication technologies (ICT), cloud computing is a technology that enables storage data or software usually stored on a user's computer, or even on servers installed on a local network, to be placed on remotely located servers. Remote computer servers are used via a network, usually the Internet. Cloud computing enables companies, organizations and individuals to deploy data and applications on leased infrastructure on an as-needed basis. Cloud computing services are delivered as one of three basic service models, depending on the level of service offered to the end user: Infrastructure as a Service (IaaS), Platform as a Service (PaaS) and Software as a Service (SaaS). There are also different types of cloud: public cloud, private cloud, community cloud and hybrid cloud (combination of two or more clouds). In the case of public clouds, the use of public networks entails cloud security risks. Companies offering cloud computing services come from a variety of sectors.

One of the original features of cloud computing is its flexibility. Cloud computing can lead to savings, notably through the pooling of services across a large number of users (customers...). However, it also entails increasing energy consumption: data centers host increasingly fundamental applications that consume a great deal of energy. As a result, cloud computing is seen as offering greater energy efficiency than in-house data centers, which could reduce the negative impact on the environment. However, because it uses shared computing environments and transmits data over the public Internet, cloud computing raises concerns about security and the protection of personal data. Some are calling for certification of cloud computing services.

Cloud services have experienced incredible growth in recent years. IT giants are proposing to take advantage of their advances in Artificial Intelligence by adding a growing number of AI-centric tools to their Cloud services, combining machine learning and cognitive services such as language analysis or pattern recognition. This is one way of making this technology more accessible to businesses, among others. In addition, the Net giants offer "*as a service*" platforms designed to create algorithmic models with minimal human intervention. This is a way of making up for the shortage of data science skills by opening up AI to a wider audience. In addition, e-Government systems are being improved thanks to cloud computing coupled with AI.

Cloud computing coupled with Artificial Intelligence enables scientists, among others, to collaborate on research projects by facilitating access to shared resources. Experts from various scientific fields are analyzing ways of deploying effective Cloud and Artificial Intelligence solutions. They are working to explore the potential of Artificial Intelligence to accelerate the process of scientific discovery, extract useful information from ever-larger datasets, and auscultate the trends that will shape scientific research in the future. In Montreal, Quebec, a Moroccan-born researcher, professor and chairholder in the Department of Automated Production Engineering at ÉTS, is conducting scientific research into the various aspects of intelligent, sustainable ecological cloud computing. His focus is on a virtual and analytical system capable of intelligently processing complex data in an energy-efficient and environmentally-friendly way. His chair focuses on three areas: i) virtual platform model for multi-tenant infrastructure, ii) incremental learning and analytics of high-volume unstructured data, iii) environmental assessment and optimization. Through its scientific research work, this Chair aims to contribute, among other things, to the creation of a new-generation green cloud model, and to unveil the vast potential for innovation in many sectors, such as public services, education, health, energy and knowledge dissemination.

Cloud computing is one of the pillars of competitiveness and one of the keys to economic growth and innovation.

Thanks to cloud computing, governments can cut costs while speeding up the deployment of new and innovative public services, but they must ensure that cloud computing resources are managed efficiently, and that the information stored on them, particularly that concerning citizens, is secure and confidential.

m) Combining Artificial Intelligence with fifth-generation mobile telephony (5G) and future 6G

One innovation follows another at phenomenal speed. "5G" technology is the fifth generation of mobile telephony standards. This wireless telecommunications technology promises to revolutionize the way the world communicates. It's a new generation, a true disruptive technology, giving access to data rates 2 magnitude higher than 4G, with very short latency times and high reliability, enabling the implementation of remote control applications in multiple fields. It also makes it possible to increase the number of simultaneous connections per area covered. The use of several key technologies distinguishes 5G from previous standards, including the use of higher frequencies and the deployment of a new generation of "*smart*" antennas.

Building the 5G network not only requires considerable investment in infrastructure such as construction, base stations and power supply, but will also lead to the transition and upscaling of sectors, encouraging investment in plant refurbishment, construction and management, system upgrades and technical training.

5G technology is already deployed in a number of countries: China, South Korea, Singapore, etc. According to the latest figures published by China's Ministry of Industry and Information Technology, up to the end of March 2020, China has already built 198,000 5G base stations, with over 50 million subscribers and more than 20 million terminals connected to the 5G network. Around 100 5G handset models have been licensed to connect to the network. 5G development has made significant progress. With the accelerated construction of the network, both terminals and products are also booming. South Korea is the country covered by 5G (launched in April 2019).

The new 5G architecture makes a number of new applications possible. Rather, it is an innovation that is revolutionizing telecommunications and bringing radical changes to the business models in use by operators.

5G offers users a very broad spectrum of uses. It supports applications such as remote surgery, massive machine-to-machine communications for industrial automation systems, the Internet of Things, drones, autonomous cars, smart homes and buildings, smart cities, cloud-based working and gaming, virtual and augmented reality, and 3D video - all services that 3G and 4G networks currently struggle to support. In cloud computing, 5G makes it possible to multiply the number of connected objects. In consumer telecommunications and entertainment, virtual reality is taking on a major role in communications between people. Communication as in Star Wars is no longer a fiction; it's now possible to talk to your present interlocutor in the form of a hologram pulled out of a smartphone. Video games are becoming even more realistic. Online video can be enjoyed with good reception quality, even in densely populated areas such as during a major sporting event, where every spectator uses a connected device. The use of consumer applications such as ultra-high-definition video, cloud gaming, augmented reality and virtual reality is expanding. Demonstration and usability trials are deepening in key areas such as the Internet of Vehicles and the Industrial Internet. A 5G autonomous delivery car is put into service on April 06, 2020, at the Beijing Institute of Technology; this car can measure the temperature of people entering the campus, recognize facial information but also make contactless deliveries. A Chinese English teacher, lecturing from the city of Fuzhou, some 900 km away, to students in Changsha using 5G and holographic projection technologies, said he has "*the feeling of traveling through time and space*". Thanks to China Mobile's 5G communications support, hundreds of millions of viewers were able to watch live on May 07, 2020, as Chinese mountaineers tasked with measuring the height of Mount Qomolangma (better known as Everest), in a forward camp at an altitude of 6,500 meters. 5G signals reach the high mountains. Meanwhile, in China, three Chinese telecom operators jointly published the 5G White Paper on April 8, 2020, jointly announcing the start of 5G messaging services, which means performing complex interaction operations in scenarios without installing additional applications on the mobile. This new mode of human-machine interaction brings countless possibilities. All mobile communications will be covered by a new bandwidth slice between 6 Ghz and 300 Ghz. Part of this bandwidth will be licensed, but much of it will be free. 5G enables better command center management in the event of disasters.

5G is at the service of local, remote medicine. It fights medical deserts. In the healthcare sector, 5G enables connected tools (including smartphones) to prioritize patients' ailments, freeing up space in emergency rooms and hospitals. Patients can be equipped with sensors connected to their smartphones, which in turn are connected to the electronic devices of healthcare staff to determine their symptoms and establish a diagnosis that is fast and as accurate as possible, thanks to the minimal latency. In China, a pioneer of the new generation of mobile data transmission, the spectacular side of the construction of a hospital in 10 days in Wuhan connected to the 5G network, during the Covd-19 epidemic, caused quite a stir. In March 2020, China accelerated the development of 5G to reduce the impact of the new coronavirus (Covid-19). 5G enables better monitoring and continuous remote diagnostics during patient transfers, for example, supporting thermal imaging for contagion control. Capable of transmitting "*voluminous*" and highly heterogeneous data in terms of format very quickly, 5G lends itself, among other things, to telemedicine activities, including MRI transmission. Image quality during a teleconsultation is sharp and precise. Academician Zhong Nanshan organized a teleconsultation for serious Covd-19 patients in Yunnan's Yuxi city on February 21, 2020, using China Mobile's Yunshixun portable video conferencing system. 5G remote medical care technology enables experts thousands of kilometers away to connect "*face-to-*

face" in high definition with doctors on the front line against the epidemic to advise on treatment. This kind of multi-party, multi-discipline teleconsultation has dramatically improved diagnostic efficiency. 5G has certainly made it easier to contain the pandemic. The countries where the fight against Covd-19 seems to be most effective are the countries where 5G is deployed. South Korea has achieved remarkable results by combining the mass testing campaign with the analysis of residents' personal data, including geolocation. Without the support of 5G, we may not be able to use technological responses such as "*Trace Together*" as effectively as in Singapore, where 5G has been deployed since late 2019. In March 2020, Huawei and Deloitte published a white paper entitled "*Combating COVID-19 with 5G: Opportunities to improve public health systems*". The white paper highlights the key features of 5G: high-speed connectivity, large networks of connection points, low latency and high data bandwidth. Coupled with Big Data and AI technologies, it can improve pandemic prevention efforts. 5G is closely linked to the Internet of Things; the network of connected objects, such as the button fitted to elderly people, is capable of triggering an emergency call in the event of a fall or discomfort. With faster, higher-bandwidth transmissions, this service could be improved. Healthcare systems with access to 5G connectivity benefit from improved response times, and enable better monitoring of patients, better allocation of their resources. 5G will be preponderant in pandemic prevention and remote consultations. In a video message marking World Telecommunication and Information Society Day, celebrated every May 17, the UN Secretary-General declared on May 16, 2020, that the Day.

"*reminds us that international cooperation in digital technologies is essential to overcoming Covid-19 and achieving the* 2030 *Agenda for Sustainable Development*",

and that information technologies bring hope, "*because they enable billions of people around the world to create and maintain links*". The UN Secretary-General noted that

"*From 5G to megadata, cloud computing and Artificial Intelligence, new technologies are powerful tools, making it possible to tackle the most pressing problems, including the pandemic. (...). Leaving no one behind also means leaving no one disconnected*".

5G also holds great potential for use in the surveillance and security of, among other things, people, personal physical assets and buildings, especially public buildings. Homes and apartments can be equipped with 5G-connected systems to ensure protection and simplify everyday life: sophisticated alarm systems, autonomous coffee preparation, waking up children, etc. 5G can also make it easier to counter cyber-attacks, thanks to improved responsiveness. In China, 5G technology is widely used in the security sector.

China boasts the world's largest IT industry. The 2019 World IT Congress, held on September 10-11, 2019 in Changsha, China, highlighted Artificial Intelligence and 5G. At the Congress, experts and company representatives from around the world exchanged views on the future trend of IT technologies and industries, and nine forums are organized on topics such as 5G, AI algorithms and network security. 5G technology is shaping the new digital economy. In China, 12 autonomous 5G buses, powered by 5G technology and Artificial Intelligence, are put into service on June 23, 2020 in Zhengzhou, Henan province, for a trial phase; some 34 digital stations are installed on the first line of this bus, 17.4 km long. China's 5G industry took another step forward with the August 28, 2020 launch of a new industrial-grade 5G terminal baseband chip, countering US attempts to stifle China's high-tech sector. The new chip (Dynamic Core DX-T501), produced in Kunshan in the eastern province of Jiangsu, is designed for industrial Internet applications and provides industrial-grade 5G solutions for industrial manufacturing, transportation and life services. According to the Chinese press, this chip features very high throughput, low latency and high reliability.

In China, IT infrastructures, which are already part of the country's "*new infrastructures*", include the 5G network, the Internet of Things and the Internet via satellite.

While all eyes are on the 5G network and its rollout, some are already turning their attention to its successor, 6G. These include the Chinese group Huawei. A Huawei research center is already studying the possibilities offered by 6G, scheduled for deployment in 2030. Among other things, it will be necessary to determine what uses 6G will open up. At present, it's difficult to imagine the potential of this network of the future, given that the 5G network is not yet active everywhere, and its potential has not yet been reached. The future 6G network should enable even higher transmission speeds than 5G. We're talking about speeds of one terabit per second, compared with the 10 Gbit/s offered by 5G. Among other things, 6G could enable more precise localization. It should also provide better support for connected objects. With 6G, Artificial Intelligence will be propelled to levels we can't yet predict. 6G will solve the problem of white or underserved areas. By reaching into space and satellites, coverage would be global, with speeds of several Gbps everywhere. Research into the sixth-generation mobile network is mainly being carried out by Chinese, Japanese and Korean teams.

n) Quantum Computing and Artificial Intelligence (AI)

We're witnessing major technological waves. Of these, quantum computing is proving to be the most powerful. This disruptive technology, which is currently little-known, is concentrated in the hands of a few "*Big Tech*" *companies*, even though its potential applications seem massive.

Quantum computing is the technology that can solve problems that today's most powerful computers cannot. Conventional computing has reached its limits. Increasing computer power requires the use of ever finer components, down to the nanometer level, i.e. to the frontiers of classical physics. In the early 1980s, the great physicist Richard Feynman was one of the first to realize that the laws of quantum mechanics could be used to simulate and better understand quantum systems with the help of other quantum systems.

Quantum computing is the sub-field of computer science that deals with quantum calculators and computers using quantum mechanical phenomena. It should be emphasized that the aim of quantum computing research is to discover a way of speeding up the execution of long waves of instructions. Specialized researchers make use of phenomena observed in quantum mechanics that are of a completely different order to anything the human race has ever constructed. Breakthroughs are being made in quantum computing. This technology could well shake up the future. In 2012, the renowned physicist John Preskill, known for his work and lectures in the field of quantum information, spoke of quantum supremacy, i.e. being able to perform at least one calculation much faster than with conventional computers, which would take centuries. From time to time, the press reports giant leaps forward in quantum computing. China has been asserting its ambitions in the quantum field since the beginning of the 2010 decade. Nasa and Google are conducting joint research into quantum computers.

China is conducting research into quantum computing. It has also embarked on wide-ranging efforts in cryptography, telecommunications, simulation and quantum computing. The importance of quantum technologies is highlighted in China's 13ème Five-Year Plan (2016-2020). China's quantum Internet combines fiber optics and satellites. China has long been interested in quantum teleportation. At a ceremony on January 18, 2017, the Chinese Academy of Sciences announced the overall performance of Micius, the world's first quantum satellite named after a famous Chinese philosopher Mozi (Micius, in its Latinized form) who lived in the Vème century BC, which has successfully completed four months of in-orbit testing since its launch on August 16, 2016 by China. So, after its successful experiments in quantum teleportation between a satellite and a ground station, China is taking its achievements towards a quantum Internet a step further. Chinese researchers have succeeded in distributing a quantum key between the same satellite and a mobile ground station: a world first! They have achieved secure data transmission with cryptography via photon quantum mechanics between a mobile station and a satellite. China continues to develop a quantum Internet that can pass through a satellite. It has established an advantage over the USA in quantum communication, but is also catching up in quantum computing. China has redoubled its efforts in its competition with the USA in the field of quantum computing. Quantum computing enables the rapid decoding of blockchain ciphers. Quantum computing is a more fundamental technology than blockchain, and both will play an important role in the Fourth Industrial Revolution. In July 2018, China unveiled an 18-qubit quantum system that exploits 3 degrees of freedom of 6 photons. China has developed the most advanced quantum computer, using subatomic particles of light (photons) to perform calculations. In many elements of quantum computing, China has largely caught up with the USA in fundamental research, but needs to place greater emphasis on coordinating the development of the system as a whole.

Researchers match quantum and classical algorithms. According to the trade press, one of the quantum algorithms did indeed produce in around 200 seconds a calculation that would take around 10,000 years on a classical supercomputer. Following on from IBM's statement refuting certain information about the performance of Google's researchers, on October 23, 2019, Google made its claims to quantum supremacy official, firstly by publishing an open-access article in the journal Nature, but also with a statement on the Quantum AI Lab blog. These are results obtained with a real quantum computer, i.e. one that is universal and can be programmed to perform a variety of algorithms, called Sycamore and making good use of 53 of its 54 Qubits. Following Google's announcement of its realization of *"quantum supremacy"*, Chinese scientists have made their own fundamental advances in this field. Researchers at the University of Science and Technology of China (USTC), based in Hefei, announced that they had created a light-based simulation, enabling them to perform calculations ten billion times greater than the largest calculations performed using traditional methods. In January 2020, the director of Google's quantum computing program warned that China could pour enormous resources into this technology, considered essential to the future of many industries.

In March 2020, the American industrial group Honeywell announced that it would soon be launching the world's most powerful quantum computer. According to a study published on June 15, 2020 in the journal Nature, reproduced in the Chinese People's Daily online on June 19, 2020, Chinese scientists have achieved the world's first quantum key distribution over 1,120 kilometers without relying on intermediate security relays. The Chinese team tested a new QKD (quantum key distribution) protocol method that uses satellites instead of ground relays. They achieved this by using China's Micius quantum science satellite to send a secret key at a rate of 0.12 bits per second between ground stations in Delingha and Urumqi, separated by around 1,120 kilometers. This represents an important step towards building a practical, ultra-secure quantum Internet on a global scale, but the actual technology could still be many years away. Chinese scientists are thus taking a major step forward in quantum technology. Quantum key distribution (QKD) is a technique used to achieve secure communication using cryptographic protocols based on the laws of quantum mechanics. Current QKD is mainly carried out via optical fibers on the ground, with a few exceptions using quantum satellites.

According to an August 12, 2020 article in LE BIG BATA magazine, Russian researchers at the Moscow-based Skoltech Institute have developed a new approach to quantum computing. They are accelerating Quantum Computing using a quantum neural network. However, there is as yet no quantum computer designed to work with this methodology. This method therefore remains theoretical at present, but could represent a real step forward for quantum computing. In the same magazine, according to an article published on August 20, 2020, IBM has achieved a quantum computing feat, doubling the power of its Raleigh quantum computer to reach a quantum volume of 64.

The race is on for quantum computers. It's worth noting that Google has been racing for years to develop quantum computers, which promise to revolutionize science through their computing power. But at present, the greatest progress is being made in the field of quantum computers, machines that cannot be programmed at will, as a real computer would.

At present, quantum computers are still very limited, due in part to the fact that they cannot run all algorithms, and their complexity, notably the cooling constraints required to ensure stable operation, makes them unsuitable for the general public. Quantum computers have the potential to revolutionize scientific computing (e.g. for the design of new medicines) and, ultimately, human societies. By increasing and accelerating computing capacity, quantum computers could transform many sectors of the economy; banks, pharmaceutical laboratories and transport will be the first to be affected.

Artificial Intelligence can be taken to a new level thanks to quantum computing. Their coupling could yield spectacular results. Quantum computing is already boosting the discovery of new algorithms. It can make a significant contribution to reducing the energy consumption required for AI learning in the long term. This could facilitate access to these technologies and give new impetus to AI by unlocking a second stage of development: intelligences based on quantum power. Artificial intelligence, life modeling and cryptography will all experience a technological acceleration.

Artificial Intelligence often aims to solve optimization problems. Accelerating the performance of these applications requires computing power. AI is a priori an ideal subject for quantum computing. Thanks to its combinatorial power, quantum computing should be able to reduce learning times and processing times for many AI applications. Major applications of AI include the detection of fraud and "*abnormal*" behavior, which are major challenges for the financial sector and community security services. Quantum computing should enable us to identify the corresponding "*patterns*" more rapidly.

According to La Tribune of August 27, 2020, which reports the announcement made on the same day by the US Department of Energy, the US Government has planned to spend $625 million over the next five years to fund research centers in Artificial Intelligence and quantum computing, with the aim of staying one step ahead in these technologies. This government spending will be matched by a further $340 million from the private and academic sectors. These funds will be used to create 12 new research and development centers.

Quantum computing is forcing us to fundamentally rethink the way we design algorithms. Current quantum algorithmic research can have a positive short-term impact. Quantum computing is a strategic technological sector. It is one of the major fields of application of quantum, along with quantum cryptography, which secures links, and post-quantum cryptography.

The disruptive potential of quantum computing is enormous. The Internet of the future will be quantum and spatial. Global competition in the coming era will be highly intensive, as it will be a competition to manage the infinitely faster advances in megadata processing technologies, including Artificial Intelligence (AI), the Internet of Things (IoT) and blockchain.

o) Security issues, Artificial Intelligence against terrorism, security through science and the links between security and development

Security is difficult to grasp in all its dimensions (physical, social, psychological, political, IT, particularly logical, etc.). The notion of security, once focused on military threats, has broadened considerably in recent decades to encompass a wide spectrum of non-military threats. Security is no longer just a preoccupation of the defense community. Crises (prolonged drought, economic crisis, etc.), which are complex and challenging, give rise to various forms of human insecurity. When several of these crises occur at the same time, their effects can multiply exponentially and invade every aspect of the lives of those affected, destroying entire communities and transcending national borders. Since the end of the Cold War, the security debate has become an integral part of the international development agenda. The international community began to link security and development issues in the early 1990s. Two important documents published by the United Nations, "*An Agenda for Peace*" and "*An Agenda for Development*", marked the beginning of political reflection on the relationship between peace, conflict, security and development. They were rapidly followed by other texts from international institutions and governments.

The quest for a concept of security that enhances the safety of people, goods and territories has led to a focus on "*human security*". The Commission on Human Security was set up in 2001 at the initiative of the United Nations to seek new ways of tackling security challenges. Following a 2003 report entitled "*Human Security Now*", the United Nations Trust Fund for Human Security was created. The Human Security Unit was set up in May 2004 to integrate the concept of human security into the work of UN agencies, and to strengthen the UN's capacity to respond to a wide range of complex crises. It helps to translate the concept of human security into concrete activities aimed at improving the lives and livelihoods of populations facing complex, multidimensional insecurity. A number of OECD member countries, including Norway, Canada and Japan, and the United Nations, notably the UNDP, have contributed to the definitive integration of human security into the global development policy agenda. Thus, human security - freedom from fear, danger, risk, despair and want - is an essential element of the development policy agenda at global, regional and national levels.

The UN has repeatedly addressed the issue of human security. At the World Summit in New York in September 2005, world leaders boldly declared: "*There will be no development without*

security, and no security without development".
This call for the convergence of security and
development policies is a response to the multidimensional crisis - humanitarian, human rights,
security and development - facing policy-makers in
the aftermath of the Cold War. On June 04, 2012,
the President of the UN General Assembly
organized a formal debate on the notion of human
security. In its Resolution 66/290 adopted on
September 10, 2012, the UN General Assembly
declares:

*"The purpose of human security is to help Member
States identify and address common and
widespread problems that compromise the
survival, livelihood and dignity of their populations.
(...) calls for responses that are people-centered,
comprehensive, context-sensitive and focused on
prevention, and that strengthen protection and the
capacity for individual and collective action*".

There is a UN Secretary-General's Report on
Human Security (A/64/701). Applying the concept
of human security can significantly strengthen the
measures taken to ensure that the transformative
promises of the 2030 Agenda for Sustainable
Development, the New York Declaration for
Refugees and Migrants, the Sendai Framework for
Disaster Risk Reduction and the theme of
sustaining peace are realized.

Safety is more than the absence of military
aggression, theft, assault, crime, trauma (road
accidents, etc.), violent events and instability. It is a
state in which the dangers and conditions that can
cause physical, psychological or material harm are
controlled in such a way as to preserve the health
and well-being of individuals and the community,
and public order. It refers not only to the control of
crime, violence and smear campaigns, but also to
the feeling of being safe from danger and the
satisfaction of basic needs (eating, sleeping,
sheltering, etc.). Threats to individual and collective
security come from multiple fronts. Wherever it
exists, poverty is a threat to the prosperity of all. It
should be noted that poverty is linked to a very

wide range of factors, including income, health, education, access to goods, geographical position, gender, ethnic origin and family circumstances. This multidimensional nature of poverty is difficult to measure. It allows us to take into account an unlimited number of problems, causes as well as consequences and symptoms of poverty. Public health security is an element of biological security, which in turn is an element of national security. The public civil protection service, which is the first link in the rescue chain, is at the heart of public safety. Safety has an important subjective dimension. This is influenced by individual and collective experience, which affects the community's sense of security. Natural disasters are multiplying and increasingly affecting human safety. When climate change and other factors converge, the consequences for individuals and communities can be devastating. Climate change has exacerbated competition for land and water in already drought-stricken regions. It undermines traditional livelihoods, exacerbates socio-economic exclusion and, in some countries, makes joining armed groups more attractive. What's more, there can be no sustainable democracy without civil peace. Many security issues are interconnected in different ways. Security is an indispensable resource in the daily lives of individuals and communities. It enables individuals and communities to realize their aspirations.

Safety is an ever-present concern for the general public. It is everyone's business. To achieve and maintain an optimal level of safety, communities are looking for solutions to the problems they face. They have set up positive mechanisms to deal with the many types of insecurity. Collective security is ensured mainly in traditional rural communities. Collective protection is deeply linked to strengthening the social fabric of the group or community. The need for public security provided by the state is a legitimate expectation for all territories. Most individuals seek security by any means necessary. The private security sector employs more and more people. Improving security as an explicit objective can therefore be a considerable mobilizing force. It is therefore important to develop a global approach that facilitates the achievement of this objective. It is worth noting that one of the main areas where a more restrictive approach to foreign investment has become evident is in national security and the protection of strategic sectors and critical infrastructure.

The application of the human security concept promotes comprehensive action to tackle the multidimensional causes and consequences of complex crises. It therefore calls for concerted action by a network of stakeholders to ensure a sustainable response to the most significant deficits in peace and development. Human security calls on the skills and resources of a wide range of actors from the UN system, governments, the private sector, civil society and local communities. By working together, these different players can capitalize on their respective strengths and existing synergies. Bearing in mind that crises have different causes and manifest themselves differently from one country to another and from one community to another, the human security concept encourages interventions tailored to local realities. In this way, major national and international programs can be adapted to the local level, so that no one is left behind. Prevention is the primary objective of the human security concept. This concept tackles the root causes of fragility, focusing on emerging risks and promoting rapid action. It enhances the resilience of local communities by strengthening their capacities, promotes solutions that foster social cohesion and fosters respect for human rights and dignity.

The issues surrounding IT security, particularly logical security, are becoming increasingly complex. There are more and more threats in this field.

The nature and intensity of threats have changed radically. The world is becoming more complex, and models for analyzing international relations are failing to predict risks. The terrorist threat has taken on a major dimension. Acts of terrorism have harmful repercussions on peace, security and development. The UN, regional organizations and individual countries are taking action to combat terrorism and prevent the violent extremism that can lead to terrorism. We are working to detect acts of terrorism and other serious crimes through the use of travel information and international databases, and the exchange of best practices on border security and management. Countries are mobilizing to meet their counter-terrorism obligations and promote South-South cooperation.

At a time when the spectre of terrorism is haunting our minds, the need for detection and protection is high. Intelligence services are based on specific rules, which are insufficient to identify all aspects of terrorism. Artificial Intelligence enables models to be built, so that the right information is available in the right place at the right time. It reduces or even eliminates the head start that always distances the attack from the response. AI makes it possible to detect the scouting phases of terrorists before they take action. Data grouped together and cross-referenced with other data could generate an alert, support an analysis or other information held by the relevant intelligence services, enabling law enforcement agencies to intervene before the fateful moment. In addition, the financial tracking of criminal or terrorist organizations faces three challenges: i) exponential growth in the volumes of information to be collected and processed, ii) diversity of sources and formats (multilingual texts, images, videos and audio transcripts), iii) analysis of sophisticated texts in several languages.

In the field of terrorism, however, concerns are being expressed about the use of Artificial Intelligence by terrorists. The growing effectiveness of AI could lead to the use of drones or robots for terrorist purposes. In their report, experts in Artificial Intelligence, cybersecurity and robotics from universities (Cambridge, Oxford, Yale, Stanford) and non-governmental organizations (OpenAI, Center for a New American Security, Electronic Frontier Foundation) sound the alarm. These experts believe that the attacks that will be enabled by the growing use of AI will be particularly effective, finely targeted and difficult to attribute. They call on governments and the various players involved to put in place countermeasures to limit the potential threats linked to Artificial Intelligence. Furthermore, in this report, the experts point out that terrorists could modify commercially available AI systems (drones, autonomous vehicles), to cause crashes, collisions or explosions.

As extremist organizations use the Internet to wage psychological warfare, spread propaganda and disinformation, and attract new recruits, researchers are developing new technologies and tools capable of automatically detecting and removing content inciting terrorism and terrorist acts. They are developing technologies for the early detection of online radicalization, to support global counter-terrorism efforts.

In many fields, safety is ensured in part by science and the latest scientific developments. For example, biosafety surveillance, where the threats are permanent, growing and increasingly complex, has a strong scientific component.

NATO has a program for security through science. Among other things, this program contributes to strengthening security, stability and solidarity between different countries by seeking to solve certain problems through the application of the latest scientific advances. It offers support in the form of grants for collaborative activities relating to the defense against terrorism or the fight against other security threats, or relating to priority themes in partner countries. It also provides support for environmental security projects.

The links between security and development are complex. Security is a fundamental human right. It is a factor in development. It is an essential condition for the sustainable development of human societies.

p) The complex links between safety and the environment

The environment is the set of physical, chemical or biological elements, natural or artificial, that surround a human being, an animal or a plant. The elements that make it up are essentially air, water, soil, natural resources, fauna, flora and landscapes. The survival of human societies depends, among other things, on sound management of the biosphere's ecological foundations. Unfortunately, the irreversible destruction of natural capital continues everywhere. Human beings are both creatures and creators of their environment, which ensures their physical sustenance and provides opportunities for intellectual, moral, social and spiritual development. The real sources of insecurity include, among others, non-compliance with environmental obligations and unsustainable development.

Human activities have altered virtually every corner of the planet, from the land to the oceans. As we continue to encroach on nature and degrade ecosystems, we are depleting vital habitats. As a result, the number of endangered species continues to rise. And human health is at risk. Humanity and its future are not safe. Many solutions lie in nature. Assaults on nature contribute, among other things, to health insecurity. Scientists have warned of the links between poor management of biodiversity and ecosystems and the risk of transmitting infectious diseases to humans, right up to the risk of a pandemic. The Covid-19 pandemic is a spectacular illustration of this responsibility on a global scale. Originating in nature, the new coronavirus (Covid-19) has shown the extent to which human health is intimately linked to man's relationship with the natural world. To mitigate climate change, guarantee food and water security, and even prevent pandemics, it is essential to preserve biodiversity and manage it sustainably.

Human safety issues are becoming increasingly complex. The issues at stake can be seen at local, national, regional and international levels, and call into question numerous scientific disciplines, including legal ones. The relationship between environmental constraints and safety is attracting increasing attention. Understanding mechanisms, identifying risks and making decisions are all subjects that call for reflection. International institutions have made the link between environmental constraints and security risks.

The UN, which has taken an interest in the environment since the 1970s and in environment-related security issues since the 1980s, is aware that the protection and improvement of the environment is a matter of major importance that affects the well-being of populations and economic development throughout the world. It has designated June 05 as World Environment Day. Since its launch in 1974, this day has become a global platform for raising public awareness, widely celebrated throughout the world. The celebration of this day helps to develop the foundations needed to enlighten public opinion and give individuals, businesses and communities a sense of their responsibilities in protecting and improving the environment. Beginning its "*environmental turn*", the UN Security Council declared in 1992 that "*international peace and security do not derive solely from the absence of war and armed conflict. Other non-military threats to international peace and security arise from instability in the economic, social, humanitarian or ecological spheres*".

The United Nations Environment Programme (UNEP) is the highest authority on environmental matters within the United Nations system. It is deeply committed to its core mandate of facilitating global environmental governance. UNEP works closely with its partners to develop scientific knowledge on the links between ecosystem stability, the environment and human health, including zoonoses. UNEP is developing good safety practices, for example, within the framework of the joint UNEP-Office for the Coordination of Humanitarian Affairs (OCHA) Unit dedicated to environmental emergencies (natural and man-made ecological disasters) and the EnvSec (Environmental Security) Initiative, which deals with environmental security issues in Eastern Europe, the Balkans, the Caucasus and Central Asia, and in which it has taken part with other UN programs and external partners. An important step towards promoting the link between environmental issues and security and stability was taken in 2002 by the Organization for Security and Co-operation in Europe (OSCE), the United Nations Environment Programme (UNEP) and the United Nations Development Programme (UNDP), with the launch of the joint initiative "*Environmental Agenda for Security and Co-operation in South-East Europe and Central Asia*" (EnvSec Initiative).

The North Atlantic Council set up the Committee on the Challenges of Modern Society in 1969, initially to deal with problems affecting the environment and the quality of life of the inhabitants of member countries. It is a forum in which member and partner countries can pool their knowledge and experience concerning the technical, scientific and political aspects of social and environmental issues, in both the civilian and military sectors. Its main aim is to tackle security and societal problems related to the environment that are already being studied at national level, and, by combining the knowledge and technology available in NATO and partner countries, to arrive relatively quickly at valid conclusions and recommendations for action.

At the 56ème Munich Security Conference, held from February 16 to 18, 2018, UN Environment organized a panel discussion entitled "*Before the deluge: environment and security in the modern world*". For the first time, the role of the environment in guaranteeing security was addressed in one of the world's most important international policy forums. The session brought together representatives of governments, parliamentarians, the military and intelligence communities, the private sector and the media to examine the extent to which environmental measures can provide solutions to security issues. It is worth noting that the 56ème Munich Security Conference has chosen as its theme for 2018, "*westernessless*"-a weakening of the West or "*de-westernization" in the* face of the emergence of new powers (China, India) and the return in force on the strategic scene of Russia under the presidency of Vladimir Putin. The Munich Security Conference was first held in 1963. Its initial aim was to consolidate commitments and better coordinate the defense policies of Western countries. Since then, the conference has evolved to involve representatives from all over the world, and now serves as a platform for various debates on global security issues.

Humanity is facing a real environmental crisis that calls for rapid and radical action. The environment is at the crossroads of security debates. The theme of the environment has invaded the world of international relations. There are clear links between national security and global environmental threats. The lexical field with "*security*" has expanded over the years. The notion of security extends to environmental risks. For example, water is a security issue. We now know that the effects of environmental change and sometimes irreversible environmental degradation are weakening ecosystems and the human societies that depend on them. The environment, as the set of natural or artificial elements that condition human life, is therefore subject to major and unprecedented changes, some aspects of which constitute safety issues. Environmental degradation and natural disasters, analyzed as potential triggers for conflict or as threats to human security, contribute to a deeper understanding of the concept of security. Environmental problems can constitute threats to state security.

Achieving an optimal level of safety requires that individuals, communities, governments and other stakeholders create and maintain the following conditions, whatever the living environment under consideration: i) control of the dangers present in the environment, ii) a climate of cohesion, social peace and equity protecting rights and freedoms, iii) respect between individuals for their values and their physical, psychological and material integrity, iv) access to effective means of care and rehabilitation. These conditions can be guaranteed by actions on the environment (physical, social, technological, political and economic, organizational, etc.) and on behavior. In our efforts to recover from the current crisis and create a better world, we need to work together to preserve biodiversity in order to achieve the Sustainable Development Goals set by the international community. This is the way to protect the health and well-being of future generations.

q) Artificial Intelligence technologies to solve ecological crises and water insecurity

Biomimicry practices have been in use since the dawn of time. Literally, biomimicry means "to *imitate the living*". It's a scientific practice that draws inspiration from natural solutions, transposing their principles and processes to human engineering. This practice is also known as bioinspiration or ecomimicry. Biomimicry draws its inspiration from various aspects of nature: forms, materials, properties, processes and functions. It is mainly plants and animals that are observed in this practice. The terrestrial environment abounds in inspiring ecosystems. The marine environment, whose biodiversity is poorer but whose species are far more specialized, could conceal the most interesting ideas. The biomimetic approach is by nature interdisciplinary. The starting point is fundamental research, which observes, analyzes and models living things. The most interesting biological models are then taken up by the engineering sciences, which translate them into technical concepts. Finally, entrepreneurs seize upon them and move on to industrial development. Thanks to biomimicry, researchers and engineers have succeeded in improving a host of materials and technologies. Drones, which can be used for combat or terrorist missions, take their name from the bumblebee. Robotics is involved in ecological issues in a variety of ways.

Initiatives are being launched to place Artificial Intelligence and robotics technologies at the heart of the ecological transition. Ecology, the science of studying living beings in their environment, is developing thanks in part to AI. The study of living beings (plants, animals or human beings) involves a huge amount of data, which it is impossible to process other than by machine. This makes it possible to simulate a real ecosystem, to better understand, analyze and improve it.

Artificial Intelligence and related technologies, such as the Internet of Things, are driving advances in most fields, including research into ecology and biodiversity, as well as environmental and ecosystem management in general. Effective waste management is one of the biggest challenges. Like any other field, the waste and recycling sector is tending to exploit the opportunities offered by digitalization. New digital technologies facilitate processes for local authorities, residents and businesses alike. Innovations range from intelligent waste containers to autonomous sorting technologies. For several years now, engineers and researchers have been developing intelligent waste containers using sensors, data processing and communication technologies. In some countries, we are beginning to see intelligent waste containers on the streets and in industrial plants, using Artificial Intelligence to automatically separate waste into different groups and compress them. A level sensor informs when the container needs to be emptied. This improved logistics system contributes, among other things, to reducing the number of trucks on the road and therefore carbon emissions in cities.

In many countries, agriculture has been undergoing a veritable digital revolution in recent years, responding to today's economic, social and environmental challenges. It is increasingly benefiting from technological innovations in AI and robotics. New technologies based on Artificial Intelligence, IoT, Big Data, robotics and advanced analysis are enabling the development of precision agriculture. Technologies such as drones, autonomous tractors, cameras and connected milking machines optimize work on the farm and in the field. These new technologies give farmers the tools to observe, measure and analyze the needs of both their farms and their employees, and enable better resource management while reducing environmental impact and waste. Artificial Intelligence brings new tools and disrupts existing processes in agriculture, where it helps to rationalize farms, optimize yields and contribute to the reduction or elimination of insecticides and chemicals by detecting disease or insect proliferation at an early stage. It also makes it possible to better measure and predict ecological disasters, in an attempt to prevent them and reduce the risk of damage.

Smart farming is further developing the tools and tasks of agricultural professionals, enabling them to meet the sector's new challenges. However, while predictability and competitiveness are two of the sector's major challenges, respect for the environment is just as important. Farmers must now be able to produce more and, above all, better. This is also the focus of many of the solutions developed by engineers and researchers using Artificial Intelligence.

Agriculture has major irrigation needs. In terms of resources, agriculture consumes almost 70% of the world's water. Climate change forecasts suggest that this figure will increase in the years to come. Every year, more and more regions of the world are experiencing droughts, and the problems and debates surrounding water use and waste are growing. Water demand for irrigation is highly variable and depends on farmers' behavior, which affects the performance of irrigation networks. The irrigation intensity applied to each farm also depends on farmers' behavior and is affected by both precise and imprecise variables. Researchers have developed models based on Artificial Intelligence algorithms and neural networks to better plan and predict water consumption by the sector. Optimal models for the main crops in the irrigation structure are developed. In this way, AI technologies help to better manage water demand thanks to a predictive tool, and to avoid wastage. Better planning of needs and maintenance operations would be particularly useful for a sector often criticized for its use of resources. In addition, the ability to anticipate water demand also enables staff to be hired and suitable electricity contracts to be chosen, thus also optimizing resources and saving on economic and environmental costs.

Water is the source of life. The fate of civilizations is intimately linked to their ability to control water. Water, both scarce and abundant, is one of the major challenges facing cities. In general, water management remains largely imperfect. In the water sector, Artificial Intelligence applications are increasingly being used for rational water management, particularly in drinking water and wastewater networks, in addition to irrigation. Advanced solutions are deployed in leak detection. Smart meters are connected; and Artificial Intelligence is used in data processing.AI applications are also used in wastewater treatment plants. The Swan (Smart Water Network) Forum is the world's leading annual smart water event. The 2019 Swan Forum takes place on May 15 and 16, 2019 in Miami. The $10^{\text{ème}}$ annual SWAN conference will become virtual and will be held from July 22 to 24, 2020.

r) Artificial Intelligence and robotics applications in the fabric of city life, airports, ports, railway stations and smart bus shelters

The world is currently undergoing an unprecedented wave of urbanization, which tends to concentrate the greatest problems of human society, but also the greatest opportunities, in cities. Social infrastructure is developed in cities: medical infrastructure, schools, municipal buildings, police stations, bus stations, drinking water, wastewater and rainwater pipes, public spaces and sports facilities, parks, prisons and courts. The services provided by the social infrastructure (drinking water, education, administrative documents, correctional system, etc.) are material and institutional supports for a specific way of life. In addition, Internet services contribute to the integration of *"social functionality"* into their products and user interfaces (connection via Facebook or Google, sharing, comments, opinions). Artificial intelligence and robotics can support the development of social infrastructure.

All over the world, more and more cities are enriching their urban fabric with digital architectures made up of sensors, computer cores and telecoms networks. This process transforms existing infrastructure systems into multifunctional information and service platforms. Because social infrastructure is plagued by human-created inefficiencies, public officials have developed a strategic vision of Artificial Intelligence and robotics that would create a new kind of social infrastructure capable of transforming city life. Indeed, AI and robotics can help lay the foundations for a future inclusive urban society, where technologies act as "*intelligent*" crutches to compensate for human frailty. AI and robotics technologies can also combat corruption, replacing old forms of power with new ones. They are tools for transforming the city's social infrastructure, aiming to promote a fairer and more transparent civil life. The social infrastructure augmented by AI and robotics increasingly views humans as information and data points, and aspires to manage the production and consumption activities of these data points to achieve greater efficiency. What's more, the development of these technologies for applications outside the city, or even the country, has a direct impact on the lives of local residents.

In a few countries (China, Singapore, Japan, USA, Ukraine, United Arab Emirates...), more and more local public officials are using AI to transform their cities, making them pleasant, well-functioning cities where intelligent safety is assured. The new established social order is aided by autonomous or semi-autonomous technology and technological decision-makers instead of civic institutions and elected leaders. Artificial Intelligence and robotics have been able to solve many problems. Robots are equipped with AI capabilities. In China, several cities are assisted by AI and robotics. In Singapore, AI and robotics are seen as solution-producing technologies for improving life for all. In Japan, Yokohama has been chosen as the "*city of the future*". This city is proposing an organized, state-supervised experiment in AI and robotics, with a view to creating "*Society 5.0*". AI and robotics are being applied to Japanese urban life in very different ways. Japanese research is looking at how AI and robotics technologies can be used to maintain the economic dynamism of Japanese society, whose population is steadily aging. Japan's "*Society 5.0*" project involves using increasingly autonomous technology to build a new human society around evolving needs, which therefore remain central. In the USA, AI and robotics applications in San Francisco revolve mainly around the growing problem of transportation. The promise of AI is to process and deliver actionable knowledge from vast quantities of data, and the promise of robotics is to convert this knowledge into "*intelligent vehicles*". San Francisco is home to many of the entrepreneurs, software engineers and multinationals creating AI and robotics present in various markets, including applications for cities. Its proximity to and links with Silicon Valley fuel a certain imaginary of urban Artificial Intelligence. In Ukraine, the city of Lviv, which is further developing a social infrastructure to achieve a certain vision of urban life that is considered desirable, is reflecting on how AI could transform its future, while an informal organization is piloting various AI and robotics projects. Here, AI and robotics are seen as tools for transforming the city's social infrastructure, with the aim of promoting a fairer, more transparent civil life. In this Ukrainian city, in the technology sector, there is a widespread belief that improving knowledge of AI and robotics, and expanding the culture of technological innovation throughout the city, would not only lead to economic growth offering greater power and independence to the Ukraine, but would also enable it to combat the corruption of the existing political system by replacing old forms of power with new ones. In the Emirate of Abu Dhabi in the United Arab Emirates, Smart Dubai is an initiative created following the vision of Sheikh Mohammad bin Rashid Al Maktoum, Vice

President and Prime Minister of the United Arab Emirates and Ruler of Dubai, to make Dubai the happiest city in the world. As part of the Smart Dubai 2021 program, Dubai Police is developing Artificial Intelligence applications and "robocops" (robot police officers). It is also striving to overcome the concerns of protected residents. According to the newsletter of August 03, 2020, Dubai is banking on Artificial Intelligence to become the world's safest big city. In the United Arab Emirates, a new smart and green city is being built: Masdar City. Its ambition is to bring together areas for research, testing and experimentation into the technologies and energy systems of the future, and to become a kind of "*Silicon Valley*" for the United Arab Emirates. Part of this eco-city is already operational in the desert.

Currently, the integration of AI and robotics into the fabric of the city to address the most pressing urban challenges shows that the culturally specific relationship between human and machine remains an essential aspect of how cities imagine themselves as communities of human beings alongside AI and robotics. The promise of technology lies in its ability to rebuild supports for the city's social infrastructure, so as to delegate more power to autonomous technological systems and be less dependent on human decision-makers, considered fallible for various reasons. New visions of cities assisted by AI and robotics are bringing to light evolving social norms and values, which need to be examined to better understand how their adoption could affect urban life. Challenges are associated with the deployment of AI systems in urban environments.

The notion of "*Smart City", a* catch-all term dominated by the information technology sector, is attracting increasing attention. First coined in the mid-2000s, the term "smart city" refers to a city that uses information and communication technologies to improve the quality of life of its inhabitants and mitigate the disadvantages of urbanization for its citizens. In smart cities, activities are guided by a certain idea of how the lives of residents should be facilitated and enhanced by Artificial Intelligence and robotic technologies. Many tasks (policing, etc.) are technically automatable, and can be performed by machines or software. The promises offered by Artificial Intelligence and robotics in terms of sustainable, inclusive, intelligent and resilient urban development are immense.

The Smart Cities 2020 global ranking, devised by the Institute of Management Development (IMD) in Lausanne, Switzerland, in collaboration with the Singapore University of Technology and Design (SUTD), singles out Singapore for its effective management of the coronavirus pandemic. For this second edition, the survey covered more than 100 citizens in 109 cities around the world between April and May 2020. IMD questioned a representative sample of users in each of these cities, on both infrastructure and services available to residents in five key areas: health, safety, mobility, activities, opportunities and governance. Given the current epidemic context, this year's survey included key indicators on how technology plays a role in the Covid-19 era. It is worth noting that the IMD survey showed that Singapore has been able to respond quickly and effectively to the unexpected challenge posed by the Covid-19 pandemic, and that the authorities' action is widely endorsed by the population. According to IMD, more than 77% of respondents said that information on decisions taken by the authorities is clear and easily accessible to all. WiFi and a fast Internet connection alone are not enough to make a smart city. Switzerland could be better represented in future editions of this ranking, as several cities there are actively developing "*smart city strategies*", including Zug, St. Gallen and Schaffhausen.

In some countries, Artificial Intelligence and robotics technologies are increasingly used in airports, ports, train stations and intelligent bus shelters.

s) Intelligent security using Artificial Intelligence and robotics to facilitate public services in the fields of security and surveillance of illegal activities

Security, in the broadest sense of the term, is about stability. It is a prerequisite for improving and maintaining the well-being and health of the population. It is the result of a dynamic balance established between the various components of a given living environment.

Traditionally, security issues have been examined in the context of "*state security*", i.e. the protection of the state, its borders, its citizens, its institutions and its values against external aggression. The security of the population is guaranteed by the protection of the State.

In the broadest sense, safety includes security. There is a certain difference between safety and security. Broadly speaking, safety is concerned with preventing and thwarting malicious acts. This means combating actions, whether spontaneous or deliberate, that are intended to cause harm. Security fights against acts aimed at profit, whether financial (theft, fraud, aggression) or psychological (incivilities, malevolence, terrorism). Safety, on the other hand, encompasses all the means used to combat risks to people and property that are not intentional. These include technical, physical, chemical and environmental risks. These risks include fire, industrial accidents, road accidents and natural disasters. Environmental problems are one of the main threats to the safety and well-being of populations in many regions. Securing the environment and environmentalizing safety is a challenge.

Safety and security are central to the concerns of political power. The modern state was built in the name of external and internal security. Security and safety are the primary regalian missions of the State. But the protection of central power is still predominant. The development of the police, the gendarmerie and the penal system closely follows the construction and consolidation of the State, but also the recognition of the individual and collective freedoms that it is intended to guarantee. The establishment of a public force justifies the law's granting it a monopoly on legal coercion and, if necessary, the use of legitimate violence proportionate to the threats it is charged with combating. The law authorizes and provides a framework for law enforcement action. There is indeed a legality of action, underpinned by a morality of action: fighting crime and misdemeanour.

Over time, the notion of security has become progressively broader. Security issues call for an integrated approach that takes into account all the dimensions of security, including terrorism. The concept of human security promotes more comprehensive, prevention-oriented action across all sectors, with solutions tailored to different contexts and partnerships aimed at helping affected populations free themselves from fear and want, and combat indignity. In the context of strengthening global national security, it is imperative to gain a better understanding of the interactions at play, to take the security ecosystem into consideration, and to lay the foundations for a coherent security system.

Safety, security and insecurity are crucial issues. Artificial intelligence and robotics are being used to prevent and control crime. In cities where cameras are used, crime is reduced and the average intervention time is cut. In addition, facial and voice recognition enable authorities to resolve incidents more quickly and easily. Facial recognition is increasingly used. The algorithm extracts a template from a photo, a sort of signature specific to each face, then compares templates from other images to determine whether they correspond to the same person. These technologies are being perfected, and are currently moving towards real-time analysis of video-protection images, enabling law enforcement agencies to monitor public thoroughfares more effectively. In addition, robots are increasingly being developed for use in private security. Often, these robots do not replace security guards, but help them to enhance site security in a spirit of collaboration between humans and technology. Robots are used for on-site patrols and doubt detection. They provide the images, but it's the humans who analyze them and make the decisions. This relationship between humans and machines has a name: collaborative robotics or cobotics. In addition, the emergency services, provided in particular by the fire department, are making increasing use of AI and robotics technologies to improve their working conditions and the quality of care provided in the field. Drones and robots are used to locate injured people or enter burning buildings. Emergency services manage a vast amount of information. Real-time data is becoming increasingly important. AI applications use data (statistics, images, etc.) to estimate the risk of a person committing a crime, or becoming a victim themselves, so that social and medical services can provide advice. Meaningful forecasts enable early detection of risks, dangers and dependencies, so that decisions can be taken in good time to prevent escalation.

Intelligent robots used in the security sector do not replace security guards. They enable them to carry out their surveillance missions more effectively. Indeed, intelligent robots are designed to be the eyes and ears of security guards. They can increase the number of patrols, and cover a site from top to bottom. If they detect a problem - intrusion or damage - they can reliably alert security guards in real time. They can also spot a fire. Thanks to their sensors, integrated cameras and processors boosted by Artificial Intelligence, robots can currently interact with their environment with a very high level of precision. In the near future, they will be able to carry out increasingly complex tasks with complete autonomy. They will be able to carry out pre-programmed missions, in particular those related to site or building surveillance. What's more, the robots' built-in cameras will make it possible to document an incident and film the individual responsible for it.

All over the world, to make their territory more intelligent, cities are being enhanced by digital architectures made up of sensors (for presence, movement, temperature, pollution, etc.) and computer networks. The result is an enormous amount of data, which Artificial Intelligence *"analyzes"* to predict and then assist decision-making, particularly in the field of urban security. Chinese cities are equipped with Artificial Intelligence technologies for mass surveillance, enabling them to anticipate threats and crimes. Artificial Intelligence shows what needs to be seen from images filmed by high-definition cameras. Among other things, it can spot individuals behaving strangely in crowds, and analyze abnormal or deviant behavior in relation to a usual situation.

A 21st^{ème} century challenge for those in charge of intelligence services, police forces and civil security services, and military leaders, is to successfully transition their field to more digital and more agile, using AI and robotics technologies. Digital transformation is influencing the field of security. AI and robotics technologies can improve the decision-making of operational managers, among others, in safety and rescue services through data analysis. Artificial Intelligence and robotics help public authorities to make well-considered decisions, to formulate priorities, to minimize damage, to take rapid and targeted action thanks to an overview of the situation, to save time in assessing the situation and to play, effectively and efficiently, their role in promoting the safety and security of people and property. A comprehensive approach to national security is needed. Artificial Intelligence and robotic technologies can tackle the roots of human insecurity.

t) Artificial Intelligence-powered spacecraft for safety and sustainable development with a human face

Satellites and space probes have no on-board pilot, and are equipped with automated systems that give them a certain degree of autonomy. Today, advances in technology and applied mathematics mean that more sophisticated systems can be envisaged, capable of conferring much greater autonomy, and even presenting a certain degree of intelligence, with advantages at stake in terms of performance, safety and cost. On-board sensors are used to observe the Earth and human activity. The development of specific sensors associated with intelligent systems contributes fully to the performance of spacecraft and their differentiation from current developments. Specific sensors are optimized to operate at the heart of autonomous systems.

With Artificial Intelligence, spacecraft acquire autonomous self-learning, perception, planning and decision-making capabilities, helping to reduce operating costs and increase the quality, safety, reliability and flexibility of space missions.

The issue of developing and implementing Artificial Intelligence in spacecraft is crucial in the field of space exploration. Artificial Intelligence is playing an increasingly important role in space mission programs. Intelligent spacecraft are also being used in the service of security and sustainable development. There's the monitoring of natural and operational environments. Thanks to Artificial Intelligence, enhanced perception of the natural and operational environment is a strategic challenge. Artificial Intelligence focuses on understanding and monitoring the evolution of a dynamic scene, anticipating phenomena and detecting unexpected or abnormal events.

If a spacecraft has the ability to change shape at any time, or to adapt to a continuously changing environment, it will be able to perform more difficult tasks in a complex flight environment. The China Space Conference 2020, held from September 18 to 20, 2020 in Fuzhou capital of China's eastern Fujian province and jointly organized by the Chinese Astronautical Society and the China Space Foundation, brought together experts and academics from around the world to exchange ideas on China's strategic plans for post-epidemic space development, key technological breakthroughs, the development of the space information industry along the Maritime Silk Road and international space cooperation. She announced that Chinese scientists are conducting relevant research in the frontier field of global space. At the conference, the Dean of the School of Space Science and Technology, Xi'an University of Electronic Science and Technology, delivered a speech entitled "*Exploring the frontiers of flexible, shape-shifting inter-sector intelligent flight*". He said Chinese scientists have been researching relevant aeronautical materials and intelligent control, and will conduct further exploration in the field of flexible and shape-variable inter-sector intelligent flight. Cross-airspace and cross-speed flight are currently the most innovative and revolutionary strategic development direction in aerospace. Flexible and shape-variable multi-sector intelligent vehicles, which use special materials and intelligent control technology, have variable height capabilities, variable thickness, variable length, wing twist and other performance features such as intelligent flight, are one of the important ways to enable humans to achieve cross-sector flight, free access and full use of space.

Artificial Intelligence is at the forefront of China's space odyssey. The country is accelerating the development of tech, particularly space AI technology. Chinese scientists are developing AI technologies that are being used in a wide range of fields: visual recognition, motion capture, space rendezvous and docking, navigation and positioning, space mission design and ship malfunction diagnostics. AI development revolutionizes China's space industry. According to Xinhuanet.com in early September 2020, reporting information from the China Aerospace Science and Industry Corporation (CASIC), China will carry out intensive satellite launches for its Internet of Things (IoT) space network in 2021. CASIC is set to launch twelve satellites as part of the Xingyun project, China's first narrow-band constellation in low-Earth orbit dedicated to IoT, operated by its subsidiary Xingyun Satellite Co. The company plans to send a total of 80 satellites into space, to complete the three-stage network around 2023. The first stage of the project is complete after two satellites, Xingyun-2 01 and 02, entered orbit in May 2020. The satellites use inter-satellite laser links, enabling them to communicate over long distances and thus improve the performance of real-time communication services. The Xingyun project is expected to solve IoT companies' communication blind spots, due to the deficient coverage of wireless cellular communication networks. Space-based IoT will have broad coverage and enable easy connection in all weathers and across multiple domains.

u) Contribution of Artificial Intelligence and robotics technologies to the fight against the new coronavirus pandemic (Covid-19)

Artificial Intelligence and robotics technologies are at the forefront of the global fight against Covid-19. The devastating new coronavirus pandemic is not just a global health emergency. It is a systemic crisis of human development, already affecting the economic and social dimensions of development in unprecedented ways. The Covd-19 crisis reinforces the importance of science and facts in informing government policies and decisions. The Covid-19 pandemic has raised awareness of the importance of science in both research and international cooperation. This crisis shows the urgent need for better knowledge sharing through open science. Collaboration is truly essential for knowledge and data sharing, as well as for advancing Covid-19 research. In recent months, the international scientific community has mobilized in response to this urgency, sharing and making research results openly accessible, and reforming its methods in an unprecedented way: major scientific journals opening the virus repertoire to all, publishing over a thousand scientific research articles in open access in response to the WHO's call, setting up international research consortia in a matter of days, enabling rapid progress, and sequencing the virus's DNA in a matter of weeks. Recent technological advances in Artificial Intelligence have contributed to better management of the coronavirus pandemic. UNESCO's Director-General recently called on governments to strengthen scientific cooperation and integrate open science into their research systems, in order to prevent and mitigate global crises.

The pandemic of the new coronavirus (Covid-19) has accelerated the transformation of Artificial Intelligence (AI), robotics and digital technologies, particularly information and communications technologies. This pandemic has stimulated the application of AI technologies, with more intelligent machines replacing humans on many occasions to reduce the risk of infection. AI is helping enormously to prevent and control the Covid-19 epidemic. It is helping to diagnose the new coronavirus. Observers say the technology is also crucial to the survival of various industries as the world continues to fight the virus.

Artificial Intelligence has also contributed to the growth of telemedicine and distance learning, and has been used to mobilize drones to deliver medical supplies. The fields of application for this science have thus multiplied, and with them the need for a global regulatory instrument. As the world is plunged into the pandemic of the new coronavirus (Covid-19), countries such as the UK, Germany, China, Russia, France and the USA are racing against time to develop a vaccine against the disease. There are currently 321 coronavirus vaccine projects under study worldwide. To ensure that a candidate vaccine is effective and harmless, it has to pass through a number of precise validation stages. The first are called "preclinical": they take place in the laboratory and on animals. Once these have been successfully completed, human trials, divided into three phases, can begin. In phase 1, doses are administered to 10 to 100 people; in phase 2, to 50 and 500 people. In the third and final stage, the vaccine is tested on several thousand people in an area where the virus is actively circulating. This is where its efficacy is tested. There are currently 132 vaccines in clinical trials, 35 of which are at an advanced stage and should be ready next year. Worldwide, eight projects are currently in the final stage of testing, after which they can be authorized for market launch. It's not the number of vaccines that matters; what counts is that these vaccines prove their efficacy and are free of side effects. It should be noted that the effects of a vaccine vary from person to person, as genes differ. It is therefore perfectly normal for the symptoms of the disease and the vaccine not to be the same.

Worldwide trials of a coronavirus vaccine developed by AstraZeneca and Oxford University have been suspended since September 09, 2020, after a volunteer fell ill during the trials. A few days later, clinical trials of the vaccine resumed in the UK after the Medicines Health Regulatory Authority (MHRA) confirmed that it was safe to use. Following this temporary halt, Chinese Covid-19 vaccine developers emphasized the safety of inactivated vaccines and a recombinant adenovirus vector vaccine. China National Biotec Group (CNBG), a Chinese developer of Covid-19 vaccines, announced that over 100,000 vaccinations are being administered and that none of the people who have received two inactivated vaccines it has developed have shown any adverse reactions, and none have contracted Covid-19. Chinese health experts believe that this is further proof that Chinese Covid-19 vaccines are safe, and a strong response to the slanderous claims made by some Western countries about the quality and safety of Chinese vaccines. According to analysts, China, which is taking the lead in the development of Covid-19 vaccines, has set a good example for the world by transforming passive prevention and control into active prevention.

Artificial Intelligence, robotics and digital technologies have helped China halt the spread of the Covid-19 epidemic. Wuhan, a megalopolis once hard hit by the new coronavirus, currently has no confirmed cases of COVID-19. China has shown great resilience in the face of the Covid-19 epidemic, and is one of the first major economies to recover from its economic impact, thanks in part to the extensive use of Artificial Intelligence and robotics technologies. As soon as the new coronavirus (Covid-19) emerged, China mobilized sufficient resources to defeat Covid-19: its technologies, qualified healthcare professionals, health infrastructures, management capabilities, etc. It was able to win this battle and manage the disease. It has been able to win this battle and manage its economy. In the cities, life has resumed or begun to return to normal.

In the face of the coronavirus (Covid-19) pandemic, against a backdrop of a gradual resumption of business activity and individual interaction, Dubai is striving to keep the virus at bay thanks to a whole range of innovations in the fields of medicine and disinfection and new technologies, notably Artificial Intelligence and robotics.

The new coronavirus pandemic is speeding up the adoption of Artificial Intelligence in various sectors, notably in healthcare and education.

v) Potential threats linked to Artificial Intelligence and the question of its malicious use

AI and robotics technologies are booming. But the problem of managing the cybersecurity risks associated with the use of AI technology, mainly machine learning, is complex. The use of Artificial Intelligence for malicious/criminal purposes is growing, particularly as AI becomes cheaper and more accessible. AI is creating new threats or changing the nature of existing ones in the fields of digital, physical and political security. At a virtual press conference on the UN High-Level Meeting on Financing for Development in the Era of Covid-19 and Beyond, the UN Secretary-General said on May 28, 2020, that attention should be paid to disorder in cyberspace as the international community fights the Covid-19 pandemic. Machine learning enables automated analysis of the functioning of interconnected systems in order to detect cyberattacks and limit their impact. There is hope for cybersecurity players, companies, institutions and end-users, increasingly weakened by hacking threats.

The growing effectiveness of Artificial Intelligence risks, among other things, in addition to leading to tools for terrorist purposes, strengthening cybercrime and facilitating the manipulation of elections via social networks thanks to automated accounts (bots). The perpetrators of cyberattacks are working to strengthen their AI capabilities. The increasing speed and sophistication of attacks is becoming worrying. Against this backdrop, existing threats are being reinforced, new ones are emerging and the very nature of threats is changing. At the same time, methods aimed at influencing populations are perceived as a reality by public opinion, particularly in the West. Hypertrucages, which are computer-generated materials, can be used to manipulate videos or audio files with a high degree of realism. The level of realism is such that the public will easily mistake the fake video for reality.

AI researchers, robot designers, companies, regulators and politicians need to work together to try and prevent the risks associated with these technologies.

w) Artificial intelligence and intellectual property

The rise of Artificial Intelligence raises major questions in all sectors. For researchers engaged in scientific research work in Artificial Intelligence, as for other scientific disciplines, a regular problem arises: that of protecting the intellectual property of their results. One of the biggest risks for AI researchers is exposing their work to academic peers or industrialists, and having it stolen. Within the framework of international cooperation, to facilitate AI research in a secure environment, in some countries, researchers from university centers have set up platforms, such as "*Joint AI*" for Franco-German research in Artificial Intelligence, which are common, reliable and protected places.

The development of Artificial Intelligence, which is driving major advances in a wide range of sectors, raises a number of policy issues with regard to intellectual property. Artificial Intelligence has an impact on virtually every aspect of creation, and continues to develop thanks to the increasing amounts of learning data available and advances that allow access to high computing power at an affordable cost. AI and intellectual property come together in many ways.

Artificial Intelligence and intellectual property are at the heart of discussions within, among others, the World Intellectual Property Organization (WIPO). This organization is at the heart of the world's intellectual property policy, services, information and cooperation. As a specialized agency of the United Nations, WIPO helps its 193 member states to develop an international legal framework for intellectual property that is balanced and in line with the evolving needs of human society. It offers services to companies wishing to obtain intellectual property rights in several countries, or to settle disputes. It offers skills development programs to help developing countries benefit from the use of intellectual property. Intellectual property rules help to reinforce the degree and pace of discovery, invention and dissemination of new AI-related technologies. They are comparable to the rules applicable to other technologies protected by intellectual property rights (IPR).

At the World Summit on Artificial Intelligence for Social Good, held from May 28 to 31, 2019 in Geneva, the Director General of the World Intellectual Property Organization (WIPO) said that 340,000 Artificial Intelligence patent applications have been filed since the decade of the 1950s.

WIPO launched a consultation process in December 2019 to guide dialogue on the effects of Artificial Intelligence on intellectual property policy.

At a conference on *"Copyright in the Age of Artificial Intelligence"*, held on February 05, 2020 in Washington and co-sponsored by WIPO and the United States Copyright Office, the Director General of WIPO delivered a keynote address. He stated that the development of policies in the field of AI and copyright raises major questions in relation to intellectual property in the age of Artificial Intelligence. Up to February 20, 2020, WIPO received over 250 responses to its call for comments on a draft position paper on intellectual property policies and AI, with submissions gathered from a wide range of stakeholders around the world.

Just as intellectual property rules must safeguard the interests of inventors, authors, artists and brand owners, IP policies must also take into account the potential of AI as a resource to support new innovations.

x) **Trust in the reliability of Artificial Intelligence systems, and the ethics of AI and robotics**: arguments in favor of responsible innovation, particularly in the field of AI research for the ethical use of algorithms in compliance with the principles of transparency, inclusion, accountability, impartiality, reliability and safety, and draft of the first global standard-setting instrument on the ethics of Artificial Intelligence, following the decision of the UNESCO General Conference at its 40ème session in November 2019

Trust is an essential determinant of digital transformation. Although it is difficult to predict the nature of future AI applications and their impact, trust in the reliability of AI systems is a key factor in the spread and adoption of AI. Trust in AI is an essential condition for getting the most out of it. A well-informed public debate across the whole of human society is needed to realize the full potential of this technology while limiting the associated risks.

Artificial Intelligence and robotic technologies are profoundly transforming the way we live and work. They have many potential applications that promise to facilitate a better future for all, but also potential risks, if they are not properly managed. Their "*aggressive*" deployment raises many ethical questions worldwide, as their use rapidly transforms the various spheres of human action. Artificial Intelligence technologies raise pressing economic, social, societal and ethical issues.

Fears linked to the development of Artificial Intelligence and robotics technologies are leading to debate and questioning. The delegation of highly responsible tasks (decisions, recommendations) to machines raises questions about free will and the relevance of human interpretation. Artificial intelligence and robotics offer great potential, but they are not without their risks. The impact these technologies could have on legal, social, ethical and cultural norms raises profound questions, particularly as regards the integrity of human life, respect for privacy and the safety and security of individuals. At international meetings, ministers, academics, representatives of intergovernmental organizations, the private sector, players in the technical community, journalists and civil society have called for the development of ethical principles to govern AI and robotics on the basis of transparency and responsibility. Researchers are working on the development of a new index for the application of tort law to Artificial Intelligence and robotics professionals.

Artificial Intelligence and robotics are forcing us to think about the fundamental rules, particularly of an ethical and legal nature, for building a peaceful and inclusive human society. Researchers are examining potential problems linked to security, privacy, reliability, societal issues and regulation.

To mark Data Protection Day, celebrated on January 28, the Advisory Committee of the Convention for the Protection of Individuals with regard to the Processing of Personal Data (Convention 108) has published Guidelines on Artificial Intelligence and Data Protection, which the Council of Europe adopted on January 21, 2019 to address the new challenges brought about by AI. These Guidelines aim to help policymakers, Artificial Intelligence developers, manufacturers and service providers ensure that AI applications do not infringe the right to data protection. A report by the Convention Committee pointed out that "*personal data has increasingly become both the source and target of AI applications*". Yet this "*is largely unregulated and generally not based on fundamental rights*". The adoption of a regulatory framework by the Council of Europe thus aims to "*foster the development of technologies that are based on these fundamental rights*" and that "*are not simply dictated by market forces or high-tech companies*". The Convention Committee stressed that the protection of human rights, including the right to protection of personal data, is essential when developing or adopting AI applications. Any AI application should take particular care to avoid and mitigate the potential risks of processing personal data, and allow meaningful control of data processing and its effects by the people concerned.

Following the launch of the European Artificial Intelligence Strategy in April 2018, the European Commission established the High Level Expert Group on Artificial Intelligence (AI HLEG) and gave it the mandate to develop ethical guidelines for Artificial Intelligence and AI investment policies and recommendations. In parallel with the AI HLEG, the European Alliance for Artificial Intelligence has been set up, as a forum engaged in a broad and open discussion on all aspects of the development of Artificial Intelligence and its wide-ranging impacts. It is a multi-stakeholder forum which, among other things, would provide input from different parts of human society to the work of AI HLEG and European Union policy-making in general. AI HLEG is the steering group of the European Alliance for AI. Following the presentation of the Ethical Guidelines for Trustworthy AI in April 2019, AI HLEG has taken into account the input received from the European Alliance for AI in finalizing its AI policy and investment recommendations. The European Commission is working to take its approach to AI to the international stage because technologies, data and algorithms know no borders. To this end, the European Commission is strengthening its cooperation with like-minded partners such as Japan, Canada and Singapore, and continues to play an active role in international discussions and initiatives, including within the G7 and G20.

At the 40ème session of UNESCO's General Conference in November 2019, UNESCO's Member States decided to launch the process of drafting a global recommendation on the ethics of Artificial Intelligence. Following this decision, the UN Secretary-General congratulated UNESCO on taking up this challenge: "*AI is drawing a whole new decisive frontier for the United Nations as a whole and for the world*". Following this decision by UNESCO's 193 Member States to mandate the Organization to draw up the first global standard-setting instrument on the fundamental issue related to the ethics of Artificial Intelligence, on March 11, 2020, UNESCO's Director-General appointed 24 leading world experts on the social, economic and cultural challenges of Artificial Intelligence to draft internationally applicable recommendations on the ethical issues raised by the development and use of AI. The Group of Independent Experts is made up of men and women from diverse cultural backgrounds and from all regions of the world. It includes scientists and professionals with in-depth knowledge of the technological and ethical aspects of AI. Among them is a Moroccan academic with a doctorate in international and European economic law, professor at the Université Mohammed V

Agdal-Rabat. The process to develop the world's first normative instrument on the ethics of Artificial Intelligence is based on the preliminary study carried out by UNESCO's World Commission on the Ethics of Scientific Knowledge and Technology (COMEST). This study highlights the fact that, at present, no global instrument covers all the areas that guide the development and application of AI in a human-centered approach.

The group of 24 independent experts appointed, in March 2019, by the Director-General of UNESCO, has begun work on the first draft of the Recommendation on the Ethics of Artificial Intelligence. These experts participated, from April 20 to 24, 2020, in online discussions for the first phase of preparation of the instrument, in accordance with the mandate given to UNESCO by its 193 Member States. These experts discussed an initial set of values, core principles and recommended policy actions, rooted in universal ethical values and human rights for the design, development and deployment of AI. They also highlighted: i) the concerns of low-income countries, ii) the well-being of current and future generations, iii) the impact of AI on the environment, iv) the 2030 Sustainable Development Agenda, v) gender and other biases, vi) inequalities between and within countries, vi) leaving no one behind. The draft Recommendation on the Ethics of Artificial Intelligence will be the first global standard-setting instrument on this important issue. The Director-General of UNESCO declared: "*the Covid-19 pandemic has led us to increase our use of various digital technologies. This has highlighted the existing ethical challenges linked to the development of Artificial Intelligence. It was therefore important for the expert group to begin work on a draft normative instrument*".
From May to July 2020, UNESCO organized extensive multi-stakeholder online consultations at national, regional and international levels. The aim of these consultations is to ensure that all stakeholders, including scientists, civil society and

the public, participate in the development of the first global normative instrument on the ethical dimensions of AI. The expert group will then present a first draft of an inclusive normative instrument on the ethics of AI, which will be considered by UNESCO member states when they draft a final text for approval as a Global Recommendation in November 2021.

At the High-Level Dialogue on the UN Secretary-General's Action Plan for Digital Cooperation, held on June 15, 2020, UNESCO's Director General, as co-champion of the 3C roundtable, invited to share her vision and strategies on the recommendations included in the roadmap on Artificial Intelligence and global digital cooperation, stressed that international cooperation is the most effective way to fight the Covid-19 pandemic. She pointed out that Artificial Intelligence is being used as one of the means to combat the Covid-19 pandemic, creating tensions between health and ethical concerns. She stressed the need to remain vigilant as a new world takes shape, and that "*we must not lose in humanism what we gain in comfort or productivity*". This underlines the importance of establishing ethical rules governing the use of AI, as it is not a neutral technology, but a tool that can amplify and discreetly reinforce social inequalities. This is why UNESCO, with the support of its member states, is working on the first global recommendation on the ethics of AI.

UNESCO launched a lengthy consultation process to obtain the views of a wide range of stakeholders. Experts from 155 countries, citizens (via a global online survey), United Nations agencies, major industry players such as Google, Facebook and Microsoft, and academics - from Stanford University to the Chinese Academy of Sciences - were all able to share their views and enrich the project's conclusions. The draft has now been transmitted to UNESCO's 193 member states, and will be the subject of a series of negotiations, with a view to its final adoption by them at the Organization's General Conference in November 2021.

The draft recommendation put forward for discussion by the international community establishes a number of essential concepts:

- *Proportionality*: AI technologies must not exceed pre-established limits to achieve legitimate aims or objectives, and must be adapted to the context of their use;
- *Human oversight and determination*: humans are ethically and legally responsible for all stages of the lifecycle of AI systems ;
- *Environmental management*: artificial intelligence systems must contribute to the peaceful interconnection of all living creatures and respect the natural environment, particularly in the extraction of raw materials;
- *Gender equality*: AI technologies must not reproduce the gender gaps that exist in the real world, particularly with regard to salaries, representation, access and the dissemination of stereotypes. Political action, including positive discrimination, is needed to avoid these major pitfalls.

UNESCO will help governments and civil society players (companies, citizens, etc.) to set up concrete awareness-raising actions and tools for assessing the ethical impacts of AI in all fields. In collaboration with all UNESCO's partners, who are invaluable allies in this process, the Organization will continue to consolidate the foundations of a multilateralism based on shared values, articulated around ethics and humanism.

It is of crucial importance to ensure that the ethical, social and political issues associated with the use of Artificial Intelligence and robotic technologies **are** adequately addressed. Human rights should always be respected, and the values of privacy and autonomy should be carefully balanced with the values of safety and security.

y) International standardization in the field of Artificial Intelligence

In today's hyper-connected world, information and communication technologies (ICT) have taken on a dominant role at all levels of life. Almost everything people do leaves a data trail in its wake. International Standards help organizations understand ICT by providing tools and methodologies that promote interoperability, security and innovation. Given the growing number of fields underpinned by the increasingly sophisticated technologies of Artificial Intelligence and robotics, the need for clarity through International Standards is becoming ever more important. The technological changes underway will have systemic consequences on the volume, content and quality of jobs, as well as on qualifications, income levels, access to healthcare and the societal acceptability of the economic and social transitions underway. Standardization is essential for Artificial Intelligence's future and its mass adoption, worldwide.

The International Organization for Standardization (ISO) is a non-governmental organization based in Geneva, whose 164 members are national standards bodies. It develops and publishes International Standards. Since its creation in 1946, ISO has published over 20,000 International Standards and associated documents. International Standards developed by the International Organization for Standardization and the International Electrotechnical Commission (IEC) bring together the world's leading experts in each field to define the most effective methodologies, representing best practice worldwide. The ISO/IEC Joint Technical Committee on Information Technology (JTC 1) is one of the largest and most prolific technical committees in international standardization.

Every year, twelve organizations hold the Global Standards Collaboration (GSC) meeting to collaborate on international standardization in the field of ICT. One of the intrinsic advantages of the GSC is its global diversity. The 2019 event, GSC-22, jointly organized by ISO and the International Electrotechnical Commission (IEC) and held in Montreux, Switzerland, in April, covered a wide range of topics, with various speakers providing expert insights into discussions on the potential of Artificial Intelligence and smart, sustainable cities. At GSC-22, the sessions devoted to Artificial Intelligence are coordinated by Wael William Diab, a technology and business strategy specialist from Silicon Valley, California, who also chairs the AI subcommittee of the ISO/IEC Joint Technical Committee on Information Technology. He said: *"Standardization is essential for Artificial Intelligence - for its future and mass adoption, worldwide"*. Speaking at GSC-22, the ISO Secretary-General said:

"GSC-22 is an opportunity to come together to share ideas and discuss challenges and opportunities. Standards are essential to promote economic development and improve everyone's lives, especially when it comes to innovative technologies such as AI or smart cities."

ICT fields covered by ISO and IEC include information security, the Internet of Things, Artificial Intelligence, smart maps, blockchain, 3D printing and digitization, and smart cities.

The International Organization for Standardization (ISO) is currently engaged in standardization work with a view to developing a common international reference framework in the fields of Artificial Intelligence and robotics. The standardization process aims not only to meet the challenges of Artificial Intelligence (in terms of robustness of solutions, regulation and ethics), but also to secure developments, without holding back innovation linked to new technologies.

On May 22, 2019, the OECD Council meeting at Ministerial level adopted the OECD Recommendation on Artificial Intelligence on the proposal of the Digital Economy Policy Committee (DEPC). This Recommendation aims to stimulate innovation and strengthen trust in AI by promoting a responsible approach to trustworthy AI, while ensuring respect for human rights and democratic values. It addresses AI-specific issues and is intended to define an implementable standard that is flexible enough to stand the test of time, in a rapidly changing field, and complements existing OECD standards in areas such as privacy protection, digital security risk management and responsible business conduct. At the Osaka Summit in June 2019, G20 leaders welcomed the G20 Principles on AI, derived from the OECD Recommendation. This sets out five complementary values-based principles, laying the foundations for a responsible approach in support of trustworthy AI, and calls on AI players to promote and implement them. These principles are: i) inclusive growth, sustainable development and well-being, ii) human-centered values and equity, iii) transparency and explicability, iv) robustness, safety and security, v) accountability. In line with and complementing these value-based principles, the instrument sets out five recommendations that decision-makers are invited to follow in their national policy-making and international cooperation, in order to move towards trustworthy AI; these recommendations are as follows: (i) invest in AI research and development, (ii) foster a digital ecosystem for AI, (iii) shape an AI-friendly policy framework, (iv) build human capacity and prepare for labor market transformation, (v) foster international cooperation in the service of trustworthy AI.

The OECD Recommendation on Artificial Intelligence also includes a provision for the development of indicators to measure AI research and development, as well as its deployment, and to provide the evidence base needed to monitor progress in implementing the principles set out therein. This Recommendation represents the first intergovernmental standard for AI policies, and provides a foundation for further analysis and the development of tools to support Governments in their implementation efforts. The Digital Economy Policy Committee (CPEN) is responsible for monitoring the implementation of the Recommendation, and for reporting to the Council on its implementation and the continuing relevance of the instrument five years after its adoption, and regularly thereafter. The CPEN is also tasked with continuing its work on AI, building on the Recommendation and taking into account the work carried out within other international bodies, such as UNESCO, the European Union, the Council of Europe and the initiative to create an international grouping of experts in artificial intelligence.

The Vigeo Eiris Group, an international social and environmental rating agency founded in 2002, has launched, in September 2019, the rating of companies' consideration of the impacts of Artificial Intelligence. The agency's method consists in measuring the degree to which companies, by complying with the principles of action defined by international public standards (UN, ILO, OECD...), manage to control the risks likely to affect their ability to create value and report on their contribution to sustainability.

The United Nations Economic Commission for Europe (UNECE) announced in a press release dated June 25, 2020 that a binding regulation on Automated Lane Keeping Systems (ALKS) for cars, including a mandatory black box, was adopted in Geneva in 2020 by the UNECE World Forum for Harmonization of Vehicle Regulations, which brings together 56 countries in Europe, Asia and North America. The regulation will come into force in 2021 in some 60 countries, including members of the European Union, Japan and Canada. It is the first binding international standard for vehicle automation. This new regulation therefore marks an important step towards the wider deployment of autonomous vehicles, for safer, more sustainable mobility for all.

China has begun compiling a national standard for facial recognition technology, at a time when its ubiquitous application has triggered heated discussions about data security. According to the vice-president of the main unit of the national team developing these standards,
"this will be an orientation and foundation for facial recognition criteria in all areas, including industrial, regional and organizational regulations".
The team is being formed in November 2019 by the National Information Security Standardization Technical Committee. It also involves tech giant Tencent, Ant Financial, the financial arm of Alibaba Group, Ping'an Group and other major companies in the artificial intelligence sector.

On September 08, 2020, China launched a global initiative on data security. This 1st global initiative proposed by a state in the field of digital security addresses key issues in the global governance of digital security. Through concrete measures, it aims to strengthen governance by clearly defining government actions, encouraging businesses to jointly assume responsibility and cooperate to address security risks. It proposes a Chinese solution with Chinese wisdom to strengthen global governance of global security and promote sustainable development of the digital economy. In the context of the accelerated arrival of the digital age, the epidemic has accelerated the digital transition of society and the economy. This initiative comes at an opportune moment, especially as data security risks are becoming increasingly apparent. The initiative is a major innovation that meets the needs of the times. With the democratization of the Internet, digital technologies such as Artificial Intelligence, Big data and cloud computing are deeply integrated into the real economy. The global amount of data has grown exponentially.

China's goal in proposing universally accepted international rules on data security and cybersecurity is to call on all countries to unite their efforts to develop universally accepted international rules on data security, create a peaceful, secure, open and cooperative cyberspace, promote the healthy development of the digital economy and contribute to the progress of human society. At a joint press conference with his Russian counterpart held on September 11, 2020, the Chinese Foreign Minister noted that his country's recently proposed Global Data Security Initiative has attracted attention around the world, ensuring that many countries have described it as constructive. This initiative responds directly to the common concerns of the international community. China and Russia are committed to multilateral and bilateral cooperation to safeguard data security and cybersecurity.

z) **Summary and general conclusions and recommendations**: Artificial Intelligence that is responsible, trustworthy, beneficial and promotes human values for sustainable, inclusive, intelligent and resilient development.

Advances in science and technological change are major factors in recent economic performance. The ability to create, disseminate and exploit knowledge has become one of the main sources of competitive advantage, wealth creation and improved quality of life. Most countries, whatever their income level, rely on research and innovation to stimulate sustainable economic growth and development. During the Covid-19 pandemic, as part of the international community's efforts to ensure global public health security, science and technology, including Artificial Intelligence and robotics technologies, are being used to combat the new coronavirus. The economic impact of the Covid-19 crisis is likely to claim even more victims than the virus itself.

Digital technologies are rapidly transforming human societies. Their emergence has improved the human condition to an unprecedented degree, but it has also given rise to profound new challenges. The unlimited possibilities offered by the application of digital technologies go hand in hand with flagrant abuses and unintended consequences. Digital divides and fractures coexist. And, in the face of accelerating technological change, the mechanisms for cooperation and governance in this landscape cannot keep pace. Divergent viewpoints and ad hoc responses threaten to fragment the interconnectivity characteristic of the digital age, and lead to competing standards and methods, ultimately undermining trust and discouraging cooperation. The IT industry worldwide is facing unprecedented opportunities and challenges.

Artificial Intelligence (AI) is developing rapidly. It is driving changes in institutions, economies and human societies, including people's lives, by improving public services, enhancing security, improving healthcare (more accurate diagnoses or better disease prevention, etc.), increasing production, productivity and the efficiency of production systems through, among other things, predictive maintenance, creating new sources of economic growth, making agriculture more efficient, helping to adapt to and mitigate the effects of climate change, and enhancing the security of property. But it also comes with a number of potential risks, such as opaque decision-making, discrimination on gender or other grounds, intrusion into people's private lives and use for criminal purposes.

Artificial Intelligence is revolutionizing the way we work and live, and offering considerable advantages for human economies and societies. Yet it also raises new challenges, concerns and ethical issues.

The intelligent revolution is underway. Artificial Intelligence is seen as a growing international security issue. It is an element of national sovereignty, a strategic weapon for security and defense.

The Artificial Intelligence revolution is unfolding like a catalyst, interwoven into a wider "*digital revolution*" that is already transforming cities into "*information infrastructures*", among other things. Over time, the tools and procedures likely to strengthen international cooperation in Artificial Intelligence and robotics are developing. At the same time, global governance of AI is being strengthened. The players involved in this governance are getting organized.

Robotic technologies are on the rise. Robots are being applied in a variety of fields. Robots could acquire decision-making autonomy, while continuing to evolve within a human-defined framework.

The hybridization of digital technology, Artificial Intelligence and robotics is challenging the traditional way in which economies, public administrations, organizations, human societies and international relations operate. These technologies enable us to make the right decision, an informed decision. The appeal of AI and robotics lies in their ability, among other things, to correct the human tendency towards corruptibility, notably by replacing human action, particularly political action, with technological action.

Humanity is at the dawn of a new era. Rapid technological advances in Artificial Intelligence and other emerging technologies such as robotics, the Internet of Things, cloud computing and megadata analysis, are turning human economies and societies upside down. They are transforming the way we learn, work and live together. The emergence of 5G and quantum computing is opening up new horizons.

The concept of safety has evolved over time. It has now taken off. It has become an integral part of all efforts to establish a climate of serenity, consolidate peace, strengthen social cohesion, reinforce democracy and promote development. It is now recognized that environmental factors have an impact on levels of stability and even conflict. Security is everyone's business. The basic conditions for security must be present in all living environments. Artificial Intelligence and robotics technologies are being developed to serve, among other things, human safety.

On a global level, efforts are being made to ensure intellectual property and international standardization in the fields of Artificial Intelligence and robotics. The international scientific community needs to make a concerted effort to develop AI that can be trusted, explained and even certified.

Artificial Intelligence has enormous potential for the common good and accelerating the achievement of the Sustainable Development Goals (SDGs) if it develops in a way that benefits Humanity, respects global norms and standards, and is anchored in security, peace and development. AI also has the potential to help meet new challenges.

Autonomous intelligent systems should be designed in such a way as to be able to explain their decisions and guarantee human accountability behind their use. Audits and certification systems should verify the compliance of Artificial Intelligence systems with engineering and ethical standards, which should be developed following a multilateral and multi-stakeholder approach. Life and death decisions should not be delegated to machines. Artificial Intelligence must be responsible and controlled by humans. Understanding change is essential if we are to thrive in a world where humans on the one hand, and increasingly intelligent machines and robots on the other, will have an increasingly close relationship.

The rise of Artificial Intelligence and robotics could create all kinds of opportunities to support growth and development over the coming decades. They could lead to a wave of productivity gains and revolutionize sectors such as health, education, transport, public services including security and justice, industry, agriculture, commerce, finance, insurance and banking. We need to work to ensure that Artificial Intelligence is responsible, trustworthy, beneficial and a force in the service of human beings. Artificial Intelligence must embody deep-rooted human values for sustainable, inclusive and resilient development.

Scientific and technological research in Artificial Intelligence and robotics, and use of AI and robotics technologies in the Kingdom of Morocco

a) **Digital illiteracy and the existence of the "*technology left behind*" at a time of accelerated technological change and the dawn of the next technological revolution**

The school education of human society is of decisive importance for human development. There is a close relationship between educational attainment and participation in social and political life. Literacy is a driving force behind sustainable development, enabling greater participation in the job market, improved child and family health and nutrition, poverty reduction and the development of life chances. The socio-economic, cultural and political development of the Kingdom of Morocco could be greatly enhanced by a reduction in the illiteracy rate. Following the Kingdom of Morocco's full political independence, the public authorities launched a nationwide literacy drive, giving impetus to the vision of a Morocco where everyone could read, write and do arithmetic. They assumed that compulsory primary education would ensure widespread literacy, and that everyone would be able to read and write more or less adequately by the time they left elementary school. This led to a policy of universal education and vast literacy campaigns.

Analysis of data from the latest general population census in 2014 reveals a drop in the illiteracy rate of the population aged 10 and over, compared with those from the penultimate general census in 2004. This drop from 43.0% in 2004 to 32.2% in 2014 is slightly more pronounced among women (from 54.7% to 42.1%) than among men (from 30.8% to 22.2%). The illiteracy rate is officially estimated at 20% in 2020. It should be noted that the official illiteracy rate, which is still high at the end of the second decade of the 21st[ème] century, is biased and underestimated because people considered literate do not meet the UNESCO definition. According to this international organization of the United Nations system, a person is considered illiterate in a language when he or she is unable to read and write, with understanding in that language, "*a brief and simple statement of facts relating to his or her everyday life*". Millions of people (Arabs and Arabic-speaking Imazignans) considered literate in classical Arabic do not meet the UNESCO definition. These people, both young and old, are unable to communicate adequately, and do not possess, among other things, the notions (of arithmetic, etc.) required to do a job or to undergo retraining in classical Arabic. They lack the skills required to function properly in human society. What's more, the official illiteracy rate would be even higher if we were to switch from the population aged 10 and over to that aged 15 and over.

At the end of the second decade of the 21st^{ème} century, compulsory schooling, advocated since the early 1960s, has still not reached all boys and girls throughout the country. There are still barriers (geographical, economic, cultural, etc.) and prejudices that restrict access to education. In addition, adult literacy campaigns have generally ended in failure. Literacy is not integrated into people's lives according to their individual circumstances. Literacy can only be successful if it is adapted to people's specific needs and requirements. This is the only way to improve their living conditions and help them find work and become independent.

Beyond the classic concept of a set of reading, writing and numeracy skills, literacy is currently understood as a means of identifying, understanding, interpreting, creating and communicating in an increasingly digital, text-based, information-rich and fast-changing world. Young people and adults lack fundamental literacy skills in the digital age; their functional literacy levels are low. It's digital illiteracy that is a huge scourge in Morocco, despite all the talk about the need to promote digitization. Functional illiteracy in the digital age of human society is a major Moroccan problem that public authorities ignore or underestimate. Digital illiteracy prevents people from accessing opportunities arising from technological progress and from navigating the digital space. Although the majority of Moroccans have access to smartphones, digital illiteracy prevents full use of these gadgets. Because of the Covid-19 pandemic, while all educational and training establishments at all levels are closed, many pupils and students, left to their homes, lack the digital skills required to engage in online teaching and learning. Others from poor backgrounds have no electricity at home. Senior public officials based in Rabat are out of touch with the realities and excitement on the ground. The Covid-19 pandemic has highlighted the enormous deficits in digital skills and technology. Digital divides reflect and amplify existing social, cultural and economic inequalities. The gap in Internet use between urban and rural dwellers is a striking example. These gaps need to be bridged through better metrics, data collection and coordination of initiatives.

Digital technologies are increasingly present in all areas of people's lives. They are radically shaping the way we live, work, learn and live together. These new technologies open up a vast field of new possibilities, which can improve people's lives and connect them to the rest of the world; but they can also lead to the marginalization of those who lack the essential skills to use them. It is necessary to rethink and improve the skills needed to take part in the digital world, and to promote digital literacy aimed at reinforcing the ability to navigate the digital space and learn to manage software, and to develop cognitive skills or abilities relating to the understanding and elaboration of information, for communication and digital social interaction. Digital literacy is the key to an inclusive, digital and resilient human society.

b) Training in Artificial Intelligence and Robotics

AI-related technologies are becoming increasingly complex, and consequently more and more difficult for the majority of users to understand. The latter are falling behind. Until very recently, there was a lack of specialized AI courses in higher education.

Training in the field of Artificial Intelligence is in its germination, or even seedling, stage. A number of higher education establishments are in the early stages of teaching the branches of AI, and are beginning to offer AI specializations as part of their curricula.

0 At the start of the 2019/2020 academic year, the Euromed University of Fez (UEMF), a privately managed public institution whose establishment was approved by the 43 member countries of the Union for the Mediterranean (UPM) on the initiative of His Majesty the King of the Kingdom of Morocco, launched the School of Digital Engineering and Artificial Intelligence (EIDIA). The university boasts major research facilities, some of which are unique in Morocco, including a 3D printing facility and the Dassault Systèmes digital platform.

Mohammed VI Polytechnic University, located in Benguérir, inaugurated Morocco's first interactive digital center (IDC Morocco) in February 2020. The Center offers access to augmented reality (AR) and virtual reality (VR) technologies to support the Kingdom of Morocco's digital transformation in the academic, industrial and government sectors. It will also help to strengthen the skills required for the Kingdom's various sectoral strategies.

At the start of the 2019/2020 academic year, the Université Moulay Ismail de Meknès (UMI) has opened a number of new programs, including the State Engineering program in Artificial Intelligence, as part of its drive to expand the supply of high-level executives in specialties aimed at the job market. The official opening ceremony of this new academic year is marked by an introductory lecture by the President of the University of Picardie-Jules Verne (France), entitled "*Artificial Intelligence: opportunities and challenges*". It is worth noting that, at the signing, on July 15, 2019 in Meknes, of a partnership agreement as part of the "*Huawei ICT Academy*" program between Moulay Ismail University and Huawei Morocco, in his speech, the UMI President declared:

"*This agreement will encourage the university in its vision of Artificial Intelligence, digital transformation and the digital world (...). It is a great honor to be associated with such a group. This alliance will enable our university to evolve rapidly in the field of new technologies, to better position ourselves and reach a competitive level*".

As part of a master's-level training partnership, the Faculty of Sciences-Dhar El Mahraz (FSDM) at the University Sidi Mohamed Ben Abdellah (USMBA) in Fez and the Institut Galilée at the University of Paris 13 have joined forces to offer FSDM a research master's degree in "*Web Intelligence and Data Science*" (WISD), and a research master's degree in "*Applied Mathematics and Data Science*" (MASD). This international training partnership will benefit from European ERASMUS+ funding for its launch in 2018-2020.

The École Nationale Supérieure d'Informatique et d'Analyse des Systèmes (ENSIAS), a leading engineering school specializing in Information and Communication Technologies under the auspices of Mohammed V University in Rabat, opened the "*Artificial Intelligence Engineering (2IA)*" program at the start of the 2019/2020 academic year. In this field, ENSIAS trains state engineers, among others. Other higher education establishments (École Nationale des Industries Minérales -ENIM-, École Mohammedia d'Ingénieurs -EMI-, etc.) have introduced AI branches into their curricula.

Hassan II University in Casablanca offers training in certain branches of AI. Its École Normale Supérieure de l'Enseignement Technique in Mohammedia, with its "*Signals, Distributed Systems and Artificial Intelligence*" laboratory, and its École Nationale Supérieure d'Électricité et de Mécanique (ENSEM) have introduced AI into their curricula.

The Université Ibn Tofaïl de Kénitra offers several branches of Artificial Intelligence. Its National School of Applied Sciences offers a specialized master's degree in Internet of Things and Artificial Intelligence for Industry 4.0, and a specialized master's degree in Intelligent Systems Engineering. Its Faculty of Sciences offers a specialized master's degree in Big Data and Business Intelligence. Tétouan's Abdelmalek Essâadi University offers several branches of Artificial Intelligence, notably at the École Nationale des Sciences Appliquées de Tanger. Its Polydisciplinary Faculty in Larache organizes a master's degree in intelligent systems and the development of decision-making systems. The École Nationale des Sciences Appliquées d'Al Hoceima (ENSAH), a public higher education institution under the auspices of the Université Abdelmalek Essaadi, which trains, among others, state engineers, offers courses in AI through its "*Laboratoire des Sciences de l'Ingénieur et Applications (LSIA)*".

Cadi Ayyad University in Marrakech offers a master's degree in Data Science. The Faculty of Science at Université Ibn Zohr in Agadir offers a master's degree in Data Science. The École Nationales des Sciences Appliquées at the Université Mohammed Premier (UMP) in Oujda offers a number of courses related to AI.

Abulcasis International University of Health Sciences (UIASS), located in Rabat and created in June 2014 by the Sheikh Zaïd Foundation in partnership with the Moroccan Ministry in charge of Higher Education, recently offers training in Engineering and Artificial Intelligence. The Université Mohammed VI des sciences de la vie

(UM6SS), located in Casablanca, offers a master's degree in Big Data and Artificial Intelligence Applied to Health.

Al Akhawayn University in Ifrane, with its School of Science and Engineering, offers a Master of Science in Computer Science, Artificial Intelligence, and has opened the State Engineering course in Information Systems with a specialization in Artificial Intelligence. The Board of Directors of Al Akhawayn University in Ifrane (AUI) met on February 18, 2020, **in the** presence of its President recently appointed by His Majesty King Mohammed VI. The meeting was marked by the presentation of the university's 2020-2025 strategic plan, focusing on the collective intelligence of the community and the corporate mindset based on the culture of performance, excellence and competitiveness. Having achieved international NECHE accreditation, following in the footsteps of universities such as Harvard and MIT, and continued to confirm its position as Morocco's leading university according to the prestigious "*QS Ranking*", Al Akhawayn University's current ambition is, among other things, to bring its academic expertise to bear on the country's needs, particularly in terms of suitability, notably in the fields of digital and industry 4.0. To mark the celebration of Al Akhawayn University's 25ème anniversary, its Chancellor and President held a press briefing on July 08, 2020. This celebration coincides with the adoption of a new 2020-2025 Strategic Plan. As part of this Strategic Plan, which is based on technical mastery coupled with social intelligence, an entrepreneurial culture, excellence and adaptability, and with a view to meeting major recruitment needs in key sectors, Al Akhawayn University in Ifrane has launched new bachelor's and master's courses. Starting in autumn 2020, its School of Science and Engineering will offer eight new bachelor's degree programs, including: "*Artificial Intelligence and Robotization*", "*Big Data Analysis*", "Cloud and Mobile Software Engineering", "Cyber-physical Systems" and

"*Decision Support Systems Engineering*". From autumn 2020, the school will also be offering three new master's programs, including: Master of Science in "*Digital Transformation*", a Master of Engineering in "*Big Data Analysis*".

École Hassania des Travaux Publics (EHTP), a leading state engineering school in Casablanca offering training in the fields of civil engineering, electrical engineering, hydraulic and environmental engineering, urban and environmental engineering, computer engineering, geographic information sciences and meteorology, is offering a specialized master's degree in Artificial Intelligence of Objects and Innovation (AIOT). This master's program is scheduled over 31 days, with 6 hours per day.

The Institut Supérieur de Commerce et d'Administration des Entreprises (ISCAE), a public institution of higher education in management, offers a specialized master's degree in Big Data, Artificial Intelligence & the Digital Enterprise. The aim of this course is, among other things, to provide the knowledge needed to decode the digital revolution, understand AI technologies and meet the demands and needs of the 21st^{ème} century enterprise.

The Institut National de Statistique et d'Économie Appliquée, a higher education establishment located in Rabat, offers the Information Systems and Intelligent Systems (M2SI) research master's degree. The aim of the M2SI research master's degree is to provide candidates with adequate training in Information Systems and Intelligent Systems, enabling them to pursue doctoral studies in one of the two fields.

The Institut National des Postes et Télécommunications (INPT), a higher education establishment based in Rabat, has introduced AI branches into its curricula. Other higher education establishments (Institut Supérieur de l'Information

-ISI-, etc.) have introduced AI branches into their curricula.

The Institut Supérieur d'Ingénierie & Affaires (ISGA) offers a course in Artificial Intelligence and Big Data. Toulouse Business School Casablanca and Microsoft have joined forces to launch an international Big Data & Artificial Intelligence course in Casablanca for students in the Groupe TBS Grande École program.

Rabat International University offers a master's degree in Big Data & Artificial Intelligence. Mundiapolis University in Casablanca has introduced Artificial Intelligence into its curricula, notably in the Industrial Engineering stream. In the digital age and the age of Artificial Intelligence, other universities are beginning to change to take account of this new situation and to meet the needs of the new Moroccan university public, introducing branches of AI into their curricula.
.

École Centrale Casablanca, a public institution of higher education under Moroccan law supported by the "*Fondation École Centrale Casablanca*", has introduced AI branches into its curricula. The École des Hautes Études des Sciences et Techniques de l'Ingénierie et du Management (HESTIM Casablanca), a private scientific, technical, managerial and professional institution of higher education with a Smart Factory Connected (SFC), is opening a new course in its engineering division for the start of the 2020/2021 academic year: "*Computer Engineering and Artificial Intelligence*". HESTIM has created this course with two options: "*Software Engineering*" and "*Artificial Intelligence and Big Data*".

In addition to higher education, basic vocational training in AI is provided by: i) Management Infographie Institut Léonard de Vinci, M.2ilv, in Rabat, ii) Handiactiv in Casablanca.

In order to enrich and democratize AI-related applications, enable rapid adoption of AI technologies in, among others, the enterprise, and address the lack of skills in AI branches, IBM has launched an initiative called Digital - Nation Africa (www.digitalnationafrica.com). This Artificial Intelligence-based platform aims to provide young Moroccans with an effective digital culture. It enables Moroccan citizens, entrepreneurs and communities with the necessary knowledge, tools and skills to innovate, design, develop and launch their own digital competencies. The Digital - Nation Africa initiative also helps citizens improve their skills to best meet the needs of the job market. It offers a wide range of courses for a broad spectrum of digital literacy levels, from an introduction to key emerging technologies, beneficial to all, through an integrated innovative section, to a targeted skills empowerment section, where users can understand the skills demands of the market and acquire proven skills to improve their employment prospects. The Digital - Nation Africa initiative offers free access to a Cloud and AI platform to include both practical exercises and enable new ideas to be brought to life.

The agreement between the Casablanca-Settat Regional Academy for Education and Training (AREF), the Department of Non-Formal Education, the Casa-Anfa Provincial Directorate and the association "*Groupe technique spécialisé en Intelligence Artificielle*", signed on December 27, 2019 in Casablanca, covers the creation of a second-chance-new-generation center dedicated to Artificial Intelligence professions at the Al Hotaya school in the Casa-Anfa Provincial Directorate. The center will target students under the age of 18 from disadvantaged social backgrounds who have dropped out of school. It will also train 50 teachers a year in the field of AI. At the signing of the agreement, the Minister of National Education, Vocational Training, Higher Education and Scientific Research declared:

"*This agreement provides a good basis for opening up new opportunities for these young people, with a view to acquiring vital skills and thus facilitating their integration into the job market. The creation of this center is in line with the projects launched to deploy the 2015-2030 strategic vision, in particular the one aimed at guaranteeing remedial education and improving the effectiveness of non-formal education*".

As part of its drive to diversify its training offering, the Office de la formation professionnelle et de la promotion du travail (OFPPT) is looking into a project to develop curricula in the digital and Artificial Intelligence professions in the summer of 2020. The project will be the subject of a technical assistance contract to be recruited by the Office on September 29, 2020.

Robotics training has a long tradition in the Kingdom of Morocco. Advanced training in this field is provided in higher education establishments, including the Ecole d'Ingénieurs Aéronautique (AEROSUP). In addition, ordinary or elementary training is provided in a number of institutes and schools.

c) Scientific and technological research in Artificial Intelligence and robotics in Morocco

Scientific research in the Kingdom of Morocco continues to suffer from inadequate funding (0.8% of GDP for R&D) and a lack of specialized skills. It suffers from a serious crisis in the production of researchers. It is very difficult for the Kingdom of Morocco to carry out its technological revolution. The Moroccan research ecosystem has a number of weaknesses. Furthermore, it is regrettable to note the disaffection of baccalaureate holders for scientific subjects. Only around 10% enroll in scientific subjects, and around 35% of science baccalaureate holders go on to study law, literature and other subjects taught in Arabic. This mortgages the future of the Kingdom of Morocco and weakens its sovereignty in the age of digital technologies and Artificial Intelligence. Moreover, little attention is paid to the social, economic, ethical and legal implications of digital technologies.

Moroccan public and private universities and other higher education establishments are only just beginning to position themselves for scientific research in Artificial Intelligence. AI training, which is still in its infancy, is not backed up by high-level scientific research. At Cadi Ayyad University in Marrakech, a professor of Machine Learning and Massive Data Analysis and a researcher in Artificial Intelligence is behind the deep-learning model predicting the daily number of contaminations in Morocco. This model is based on machine learning, and enables problem-solving to be learned from examples or past experience, thanks to an algorithm using artificial neural networks.

The National Center for Scientific and Technical Research (CNRST) under the Ministry of National Education, Vocational Training, Higher Education and Scientific Research only launched the first call for research projects in the field of Artificial Intelligence and its Applications in March 2019. This call in the Al-Khawarizmi Research Support Program is launched in partnership with the Ministry of Industry, Commerce and the Green and Digital Economy, with funding of 50 million DH.

In the Al-Khawarizmi Program to support research in the field of Artificial Intelligence and its Applications, the main research themes concern..:
- Education and pedagogical approaches: personalized learning models; automatic tutoring systems; dropout prevention; detection of learning disabilities; intelligent teacher assistance modules; etc.

- Health: precision medicine; robotic surgery; medical imaging and telemedicine; expert systems for early diagnosis; e-Health; patient care; development of new molecules; etc.
- Agriculture: precision farming; smart farms; etc.
- Finance, banking and insurance: rating model enabling access to credit for under-served segments (SMEs, VSEs); product recommendation system; preventive management of customer loss; fraud prediction and identification; autonomous pricing system; blockchain; digital currency; etc.
- Energy, water and environment: Smart Grids; energy efficiency; intelligent water management systems; environmental monitoring systems; etc.
- Industry: predictive maintenance; robotics; industry 4.0; etc.
- Transport and logistics: intelligent urban mobility; autonomous connected vehicles; smart supply chain; etc.
- Telecommunications and networks: targeted marketing maximizing ROI through multi-variable modeling; product recommendation system; preventive customer loss management; capex deployment optimization; security; etc.
- Computer vision: urban security and video protection; robotics; video games; etc.
- Natural Language Processing (NLP): machine translation; machine interpreting; machine dialog; machine reasoning; machine learning; etc.
- Smart cities: smart homes; smart buildings; urban mobility; energy efficiency; security; etc.
- Regional planning: territorial intelligence; desertification; etc.
- Tourism: smart tourism; contextualized, personalized recommendations in natural language; chatbots for advice, activities, etc.; equipment control; automatic production of editorial content; etc.
- Digital security and trust: digital security; encryption; electronic signature; etc.
- Justice: predictive justice; Artificial Intelligence in legal knowledge management; automatic extraction of information from databases and legal texts; automatic classification and summarization

of legal text; e-Justice; Data Mining applied to the legal field; etc.
- Big Data.

The initiative of the Ministry of National Education, Vocational Training, Higher Education and Scientific Research, via the CNRST, is commendable, but the effort remains modest compared to the strategic nature of AI and robotic technologies, on which the future development of the Kingdom of Morocco and all countries will depend. Those who master the technologies of the future will dominate the world. In addition, the Ministry of National Education, Vocational Training, Higher Education and Scientific Research recently acquired a very powerful computer with high computing capacities. The use of this computer, located at the CNRST, is open to researchers from both public and private Moroccan universities, and even from friendly countries. The aim of this program is to adapt AI to Moroccan contexts, with a view to generating real socio-economic impact.

In a press release dated April 14, 2020, the Hassan II Academy of Science and Technology called for prospective research to be prioritized, and for efforts to be focused on actions that could save lives and facilitate diagnosis of Covid-19 infection. She proposed, among other things, to set up a multi-disciplinary working group in the fields of epidemiological studies in general, and data analysis, using digital engineering and Artificial Intelligence in particular, in relation to the conditions of expansion of the Covid-19 epidemic, and with therapeutic management protocols and patient evolutions. As part of the Kingdom of Morocco's efforts to combat the new coronavirus pandemic (Covid-19), in a press release dated May 04, 2020, as part of its scientific plan, the Hassan II Academy of Sciences and Techniques has released a budget of 10 million DH, and launched in June 2020, a call for research projects on three major themes, among others, mathematical modeling and Artificial Intelligence in the fight against Covid-19.

As part of their scientific activities, higher education establishments occasionally present the limited results of their AI research work at seminars, colloquia and conferences held in Morocco. Sometimes, the speakers come from abroad. Here are a few examples. As part of its conference cycle, the Institut Supérieur d'inGénierie & des Affaires (ISGA) organized, on March 1, 2018, at ISGA's Marrakech center, a conference-debate on the theme: "*Artificial Intelligence: What impact on systems governance?*". Mohammed V University in Rabat has organized, in partnership with the Ministry of National Education, Vocational Training, Higher Education and Scientific Research, on March 16, 2019 in Rabat at the École Nationale Supérieure d'Informatique et d'Analyse des Systèmes (ENSIAS), a conference-debate on the theme: "*The challenges of Artificial Intelligence (AI) for education and training*". On the occasion of International Mathematics Day, as part of its scientific activities, the Laboratory of Applied Sciences (LSA) at the National School of Applied Sciences in AL Hoceima had planned to organize its first scientific day on March 28, 2020. However, this event has been postponed due to the Covid-19 pandemic.

In a press release dated December 11, 2019, the ENACTUS team at the École Mohammadia des Ingénieurs (EMI), which is affiliated to Mohammed V University in Rabat, announced the deployment of the I-TERRA project, a social entrepreneurship aimed at targeting, automating and optimizing the irrigation of agricultural land in Morocco. The project consists of a control station that collects a range of information, including air and soil humidity, UV radiation and atmospheric pressure. The solution automatically controls the irrigation system using Artificial Intelligence decision-making algorithms, based on the data collected by the sensors. The École Mohammadia d'Ingénieurs (EMI) and the Association des Ingénieurs de l'EMI (AIEM) have organized a new edition of the Challenge Projets d'Entreprendre, from October 19 to 26, 2019, on the theme "*Intelligent solutions for societal challenges*".

As part of the fight against the Covid-19 pandemic, the Kingdom of Morocco has decided to take up a major challenge: the manufacture of the first 100% Moroccan artificial respirator. This device is indispensable in intensive care for severe cases of Covid-19. On the instructions of His Majesty the King, may God assist Him, all Moroccan skills in the public and private sectors that can contribute to making this equipment available to the Ministry of Health are being sought. Doctors, experts and engineers, particularly from the aeronautical sector, set to work designing a respirator. Successive versions were improved. On May 08, 2020 in Casablanca, the Foundation for Research, Development and Innovation in Science and Engineering (FRSDISI) presented a 100% Moroccan artificial intelligent respirator, designed to meet the needs of medical centers catering for people with respiratory problems. This respirator, Nafas, whose patent is registered with the Moroccan Office of Industrial and Commercial Property (OMPIC), is the product of collaboration with a committee of doctors comprising a team from the Mohammed VI University of Health Sciences (UM6SS) and a doctor from the military health service of the Royal Armed Forces (FAR). Several respirator versions are available. The Société d'Etudes et de Réalisations Mécaniques de Précision (SERMP), a subsidiary of the French Le Piston group specializing in the manufacture of aeronautical parts and assemblies, has set up an "*ephemeral factory*" inside its Nouaceur unit to house the assembly of respirators designed and assembled by 100% Moroccan skills. The Nafas prototype will be presented to the Minister of

Industry, Commerce and the Green and Digital Economy on June 15, 2020.

Morocco's first private institution for high-level, multidisciplinary scientific research, Institut Scientifique Terjaoui International de la Bonne Gouvernance et de la Planification Stratégique du Développement Humain Durable, abbreviated to Institut Scientifique ISTIGOP, is passionate about disruptive technologies such as Artificial Intelligence, robotics, nanotechnologies, biotechnologies, genetics, IT and cognitive sciences, as well as their pollination, passionate about disruptive technologies such as Artificial Intelligence, robotics, nanotechnologies, biotechnologies, genetics, IT and cognitive sciences, as well as their cross-pollination and impact on human society, is a pioneer in AI research. The ISTIGOP Scientific Institute has been focusing on the development of Artificial Intelligence and its applications since its creation in January 2012. The Institute has set up, among other things, the International Observatory on the Technological, Economic and Societal Impacts of Artificial Intelligence (AI), and an Artificial Intelligence Research Unit attached to the Centre d'Études et de Recherches Pluridisciplinaires. The ISTIGOP Scientific Institute covers all aspects of AI at 360°. It assesses the performance of AI systems, in areas such as reliability, robustness, efficiency, achievement of societal goals and equity. The ISTIGOP Scientific Institute examines the economic, ethical, political and legal repercussions of Artificial Intelligence on human societies. It examines the impact of AI on different groups of people and sectors of activity. It scrutinizes knowledge on the societal impacts of AI. The ISTIGOP Scientific Institute reflects on the opportunities and challenges that AI and related technologies pose for governments, organizations, human societies and citizens.

The MAScIR Foundation (Moroccan Foundation for advanced science, innovation and research) is focusing on AI-related issues, with the creation of the Embedded Systems and Artificial Intelligence Center.

The Fédération Marocaine des Technologies de l'Information, des Télécommunications et de l'Offshoring (APEBI) has launched its series of meetings dedicated to the community of ICT professionals. On June 11, 2020, its "*industry 4.0*" cluster organized the thematic webdialogue on the theme "*Role of the Digital Ecosystem in the industrial revival of post-covid Morocco*". An integral part of the federation's new organization since the start of the current 2020-2022 mandate, the Industrie 4.0 Cluster aims to federate the Ecosystem and create a community of ICT and digital operators, proposing offers in industry 4.0, but also to build a space for exchanging best practices. It should be noted that the concept of Industry 4.0 or industry of the future corresponds to a new way of organizing means of production; the aim is to set up smart factories capable of greater adaptability in production and more efficient allocation of resources, thus paving the way for a new industrial revolution. Its technological foundations are the Internet of Things and cyber-physical systems. Industry 4.0 brings enormous productivity and quality gains to the industry.

Scientific research in AI in the Kingdom of Morocco is still very rudimentary and fragmented. They are organized mainly outside universities and higher education institutions. For example, the Moroccan office of McKinsey & Company organized, July 20, 2018 in Casablanca, a meeting in the field of digital and Artificial Intelligence to identify the challenges and impact of new developments in this field on the economies of the African continent and specifically Morocco. On April 17, 2019 in Casablanca, the Moroccan representative of global analytics leader SAS presented its investment plan in Artificial Intelligence and its new investment program dedicated to the African market. Its aim is to bring the Group's various solutions to Africa. Morocco is a key location for SAS.

In the Kingdom of Morocco, scientific and technological research into Artificial Intelligence and robotics is still limited. AI research and development is characterized by a network of obstacles of all kinds, including political, budgetary and economic. Artificial Intelligence research is characterized, among other things, by low budgets, insufficient individual and institutional capabilities, and low and fragmented investment.

Artificial Intelligence, which gives rise to hopes and concerns on technical, economic and social levels, brings to the fore heavy questions to which answers can only be found within the framework of an enlightened debate on human society. Research in the humanities and social sciences will make an essential contribution to this debate.

A national Artificial Intelligence strategy is needed. The Kingdom of Morocco has the necessary resources (mathematicians) to develop and implement this meaningful national AI strategy, which will serve as a growth driver for decades to come.

d) Scientific and technological cooperation in AI with foreign partners, particularly European countries and China

Within the framework of bilateral and multilateral regional cooperation with the European Union, scientific and technological cooperation in the field of Artificial Intelligence between Moroccan institutions, particularly higher education establishments and their foreign partners, is very rudimentary. The partnership is limited, broadly speaking, to the organization of training at Master's level.

The Mohammed VI Polytechnic University of Benguerir and UNESCO organized a Forum on Artificial Intelligence in Africa from December 12 to 13, 2018 in Benguerir. This Forum is organized in in partnership with UNESCO member states, the African Union (AU), Africa's Regional Economic Communities (RECs), the Office Chérifien des Phosphates (OCP) and its Foundation, Microsoft Africa and China's International Center for Cultural Communication. The Forum, which included plenary sessions and thematic workshops, explored the opportunities and challenges presented by these technological innovations in the African context. Participants debated themes relating to "*AI in Africa: issues, challenges and opportunities*", "*What future for AI in Africa*", "*Universal access to information and knowledge and AI in Africa*" and "*AI, a development lever for youth in Africa*".

The Hassan II Academy of Sciences and Technology and the Chinese Academy of Sciences renewed their partnership in the field of scientific and academic research on November 21, 2019 in Rabat. The main aim of the new agreement is to strengthen the academic collaboration and exchange of scientific and technological expertise conducted since 2012. It expresses the strong commitment of both countries and institutions to developing and strengthening cooperation in Artificial Intelligence, technology sciences and global warming. The new agreement will enable the Hassan II Academy of Science and Technology to benefit from Chinese expertise in Artificial Intelligence, where the Academy plans to set up large dedicated laboratories.

As part of its exploration of the great regions of the world and the theme of its 45ème session devoted to "*Latin America, as a horizon of thought*", the Academy of the Kingdom of Morocco inaugurated its lecture series on November 22, 2017 in Rabat. Thus, the former President of Brazil, Collor de Mello, during his lecture whose theme is "*Latin America, as a horizon of thought: Sailors' or castaways' courses?*", as a prelude to this session, he pleaded for a rapprochement between Morocco and the countries of Latin America. He declared:

"Today, in the *age of so-called "industry 4.0", it's the attention that will be paid to the major trends of the day, such as: nanotechnologies, internet of things, algorithms, quantum computers, Artificial Intelligence, robotics, etc. that will determine the leaders of tomorrow*".

As part of the *"Académie française au Maroc"* lecture series, speaking at a conference organized, on May 02, 2019 in Rabat, by the Académie du Royaume du Maroc in partnership with the Académie française, on the theme *"Le passage du XXe au XXIe siècle"*, French academician Gabriel De Broglie traced the specific features of the transition from the XXème to the XXIème century, focusing on the digital revolution, the ambivalence of globalization, humanism and the challenge of materialism. He pointed out that Artificial Intelligence has been able to connect not only data to Man, but data to data, enabling virtual exchanges, hotel reservations and corporate recruitment. The French academician noted that Artificial Intelligence is likely to surpass the will of Man, and pointed out that *"technological singularity"* is the hypothesis that the invention of Artificial Intelligence would trigger a runaway surge in technological growth that would induce unpredictable changes in human society.

Moroccan institutions also organize events with their international partners. A few examples. As part of its relations with its partners based abroad, the Hassan II Academy of Science and Technology organized, on March 26, 2018 in Rabat, a conference entitled "*Renaissance and current promises of Artificial Intelligence*" and given by Jean-Gabriel GANASCIA Professor at Pierre et Marie Curie University - Paris, Chairman of the CNRS Ethics Committee - France. On March 27, 2019, Université Mohammed VI des Sciences de la

Santé organized, in partnership with Global Santé and Université Paris 13 Panthéon Cité, its first international French-language symposium on the theme of "*Artificial Intelligence in the health sciences, from dream to reality: what opportunities for Morocco?*". This scientific event brought together researchers and industrialists working in Artificial Intelligence in the health sciences.

On February 15 and 16, 2019, the Polydisciplinary Faculty of Larache organized the 3ème edition of the international conference "*Journées Scientifiques en Sciences Appliquées - JSSA'19*". During the two-day event, topics covered included Artificial Intelligence and Neural Computing, Big Data Analytics and Smart City. The "*Signals, Distributed Systems and Artificial Intelligence*" laboratory at the École Normale Supérieure de l'Enseignement Technique de Mohammedia (ENSET - M) organized, from December 16 to 18, 2019, in collaboration with its national and international partners and with the support of Hassan II University of Casablanca (UH2C), three scientific days with open doors. The discussion day on December 16 is organized around the theme "*Robotics training in the era of Industry 4.0: Issues and Challenges*". On December 17, the laboratory organized its doctoral day on the theme of "*Telecommunications and Artificial Intelligence in the service of digitalization*".

The Institut Supérieur d'inGénierie & des Affaires (ISGA) organized a webinar on "*Chatbots: effet de mode ou révolution*" on May 28, 2020 at ISGA's Fez center, in collaboration with the Unité de formation et de recherche (UFR) des sciences de l'ingénieur de l'Université Bretagne Sud.

As part of the fight against the Covid-19 pandemic, following an international call for projects launched by the Agence Universitaire de la Francophonie (AUF) for the development of solutions with an immediate technological and/or social impact to help healthcare systems and populations cope with this unprecedented health crisis, the project by the Université Chouaïb Doukkali d'El Jadida has been awarded a prize. This supported project consists of a rapid serological test to detect the presence of anti-Covid-19 antibodies, using a Smart BIOCAPTeur integrating Cloud computing technology (SMARTBIOCAPT).

Al Akhawayn University in Ifrane is forging a partnership with New York University (NYU), where a Moroccan-born professor and Al Akhawayn University laureate has recently designed an Artificial Intelligence tool to understand the evolution of the Coronavirus and determine the actions to be taken to limit its impact. This decision-support tool, based mainly on predictive analysis, makes it possible to
"*report the clinical severity of pandemic-infected cases and will help doctors determine which patients really need beds and which can go home, as hospital resources are limited*".
The partnership between the two universities, through this Moroccan-born professor, will enable the use of advanced technologies to track the spread of Covid-19 in the Kingdom of Morocco, and to accurately determine its economic and health impacts.

In early May 2020, a group of international researchers (two French, one Brazilian, one Lebanese, one German, two Canadians and one Moroccan) launched the interactive platform "*Epitopes.world*" powered by Artificial Intelligence, with the aim of accelerating the development of a coronavirus vaccine.

From October 07 to 09, 2020, the Computer Engineering Department of the Faculty of Science and Technology in Tangier will be organizing the Fifth International Conference on Smart City Applications. The conference is being organized in partnership with the Computer Engineering Department of the Faculty of Engineering at

Karabuk University (Turkey) and the Mediterranean Association of Science and Technology (Medi-AST). The aim of the conference is to bring together researchers and industrial engineers to discuss and exchange experimental and theoretical results, new models, case studies and innovative ideas in the field of smart cities.

The 5ème international conference on "*Cloud Computing and Artificial Intelligence: technologies and applications*", organized by the École Nationale Supérieure d'Informatique et d'Analyse des Systèmes (ENSIAS), will be held from November 24 to 26, 2020 in Marrakech. It is a high-level international forum to present cutting-edge research results, address new challenges and discuss trends and opportunities related to all aspects and applications of Cloud technology, Artificial Intelligence, Big Data, High-Performance Computing and the Internet of Things.

e) Overview of the use of Artificial Intelligence and robotic technologies

The coronavirus crisis is currently showing just how important digitization is in public administrations, the healthcare sector, schools, businesses and homes, among others. The Kingdom of Morocco must put all its energy into driving forward digital innovations. This is important for competitiveness and future jobs, among other things. Morocco is moving towards a data economy for the future.

Artificial Intelligence and robotics technologies are on the rise. In the era of a new technological revolution with major economic and social implications, where digital technology is transforming businesses and institutions, Artificial Intelligence in the Kingdom of Morocco will affect all sectors of economic, social, cultural and administrative activity, particularly public institutions. The prospects offered by Artificial Intelligence to public officials, professionals, organizational players and individuals are infinite. All sectors are potentially concerned. But upstream research into AI is still rudimentary.

Artificial Intelligence is increasingly present in people's daily lives, thanks to their favorite devices, smartphones, but it is currently relatively little exploited there. In the long term, smartphones will be able to perform tasks on their own.

A number of Moroccan organizations, mainly large corporations, are embarking on emerging technologies such as Artificial Intelligence. More and more companies (banking, telecoms, insurance, manufacturing, modern farming, energy, automotive, etc.) are turning to analytics and Artificial Intelligence, using AI mechanisms in a wide range of applications. The promotion of AI is a lever for economic development and a tool for transforming organizations. Some startups are playing the AI card. The stakes of AI are enormous. The productivity gains are enormous.

In the age of digitalization and Artificial Intelligence, RAM, which continues to offer new services in harmony with the needs of its customers, has launched, in April 2019, a new robotized and instantaneous information service via WhatsApp. It thus becomes the first airline on the African continent to offer this service. In a press release published in the last week of May 2020, Attijariwafa Bank launched a chatbot available via its institutional website to provide help and information online 24/7. This is a first in Morocco. The virtual assistant set up by Attijariwafa Bank, based on Artificial Intelligence, enables its customers to conduct an interactive dialogue, getting answers to their questions quickly and efficiently. This service supports the Customer Relations Centre, which is in great demand during this period of health crisis. In addition, BMCE

Capital, the Business Banking Division of the Bank Of Africa Group, announced in a press release on June 08, 2020, the launch of an innovative new service reserved initially for customers of the Asset Management business, BMCE Capital Gestion. This is the first chatbot in the marketplace, dubbed "*BK Financial Bot*", dedicated to the investment banking business, the fruit of the CAP'Tech by BMCE Capital open innovation program. This conversational agent makes it possible to instantly receive key information on investments and mutual fund operations on WhatsApp. This free chatbot is available 24/7, and has the added advantage of being scalable. It will be enhanced in the coming weeks with new services covering other investment banking businesses. For its part, Banque marocaine pour le commerce et l'industrie (BMCI) announced on June 08, 2020, the launch of a chatbot, certified by Facebook since May 2020, with a view to establishing an interactive dialogue with its customers and prospects. According to BMCI's press release, its chatbot makes it possible to respond efficiently and quickly to different types of request depending on the user's profile, and to handle queries relating to, among other things, the measures taken by BMCI for its customers in the exceptional circumstances of the health crisis, the benefits served by the CNSS and those of RAMED and non-RAMED, credit deferrals and bank cards. These requests can be processed in French as well as in dialectal Arabic (Darija) and classical Arabic. In its press release, BMCI emphasized that this innovative solution had been designed and created thanks to the joint expertise of BMCI's innovation teams and BNP Paribas Group's LAB innovation IRP. On June 09, 2020, the Al Omrane Group launched Morocco's first multi-language, multi-platform chatbot at the service of citizens. This virtual assistant, based on Artificial Intelligence, provides instant and permanent access to information in French, classical Arabic and Darija. Accessible 24/7 via the holding's website and WhatsApp and Facebook platforms, the assistant complements the various communication channels set up by the Group. In its press release, the Al Omrane Group emphasized that it has readapted its Digital Roadmap to incorporate a special "*Mouwakaba*" program to accelerate digitalization, "*in line with the momentum of national commitment instilled by His Majesty King Mohammed VI and aimed at safeguarding the health of citizens*".

Moroccan financial services do not yet fully apply Artificial Intelligence and robotics technologies. These services could leverage AI for, among other things, fraud detection, borrower credit assessment, customer service cost reduction, automated trading and regulatory compliance.

In the healthcare sector, AI systems, notably at the Université Mohammed VI des Sciences de la Vie, are helping to diagnose and prevent diseases and epidemics as early as possible, discover treatments and drugs, or propose personalized interventions; in addition, they are paving the way for self-monitoring tools. In addition, the new intelligent video surveillance thermal technology, which measures thermal radiation throughout the image area and assigns a temperature value to each pixel, can help analyze critical situations during epidemics such as Covid-19, through a high-performance camera. As part of efforts to combat Covid-19, a Moroccan security company launched a locally designed and manufactured automatic hygiene bag in September 2020. This invention ensures automatic temperature control and gel dispensing without human intervention. The machine thus provides effective prevention against the spread of bacteria and viruses by ensuring that hands are washed each time they enter the secure area.

In the field of agriculture, on modern farms, Artificial Intelligence helps monitor crop and soil conditions, improve irrigation and predict the impact of environmental factors on crop yields. In a press release published on June 26, 2020, the Institut National de la Recherche Agronomique (INRA) forged a partnership with SOWIT, a company specializing in the use of Artificial Intelligence for the development of African agriculture, to optimize agricultural crop management and streamline decision-making processes on a spatial, plot and territorial scale.

Artificial intelligence and robotic technologies are beginning to perfect building construction processes. The Allianz Maroc (ex-Zurich) building is the first smart building in Casablanca, the Kingdom's economic capital. In a smart building, digital technologies ensure intelligent control of all energy functions and electrical appliances. Data is the key to intelligent building operation. Equipping a building with sensors is all very well, but knowing how to analyze the data is even better. A computerized system, called building management system (BMS), is installed in the building to supervise all the equipment installed there. This system provides an overall view of the building's operation and automation systems.

In the Kingdom of Morocco, the need to build smart cities is increasingly being raised. Events (conferences, symposia, seminars, exhibitions, etc.) on this subject are being organized. The smart city is a city that uses new information and communication technologies and AI technologies for the benefit of its citizens, in order to meet their needs efficiently and responsibly. Faced with the challenges of urban development and demographic growth specific to developing countries, the smart city concept is particularly relevant in Africa. Through its economic capital, Casablanca, Morocco aspires to become a benchmark for smart cities on the continent. The Moroccan city aims to become a "*smart city*". Digital transformation is at the heart of the major projects undertaken by the economic capital as part of the Greater Casablanca Development Plan 2015-2020. The flagship projects of this transformation include the

"*Casa smart City*" project, which is at the heart of Greater Casablanca's Digital Transformation Master Plan. Among other things, this smart city aims to reduce and optimize the city's operating costs, improve the quality of services provided to users, develop "*tech-champions*" and contribute to the city's influence and appeal. Following a call for tenders, Casablanca has chosen IDATE and IT consulting to help it implement its Digital Transformation Master Plan. Morocco's largest city is playing a leading role within the Kingdom in the modernization of urban space. Since October 2015, Casablanca has been the first African city to join the network of twenty-five smart cities selected by the Institute of Electrical and Electronics Engineers (IEEE3), the world's largest association of digital and information technology professionals. Applications of AI technologies in Casablanca, which aims to become a Smart city, are still limited. As an example, when it comes to waste collection, which poses a huge problem, we can do as the city of Shanghai in China has done, using megadata and smart devices to help sort waste. It's worth noting that Shanghai, the first city on the Chinese mainland to introduce mandatory waste classification regulations in July 2019, uses intellectual platforms (smart bins...) to count the amount of waste stored by residents in order to improve recycling.

The e-Madina, created in June 2013 by the Moroccan Federation of Information Technology, Telecommunications and Offshoring (APEBI) as a think tank on smart cities, subsequently opened up to public and private players outside the information and telecommunications fields, from different business sectors, interested in solving urban issues. In 2014, e-Madina opted for a Smart City 4P model (Public-Private-People-Partnership), which takes into account all the players in the urban ecosystem, including the citizen, to operate the transformation of the city. e-Madina also relies on international and research partnerships, to benefit from existing benchmarks and academic advances. In April 2015, e-Madina was transformed into a Smart City Cluster. The Cluster was officially launched with the support and endorsement of the Wilaya du Grand Casablanca, the City of Casablanca and the Greater Casablanca region. The Smart City Cluster works to make the city of Casablanca more attractive, more efficient and more competitive, for businesses, citizens and visitors alike, through partnerships between public and private sector players and civil society, and through the use of technology.

On the outskirts of Casablanca, the Zenata Eco-City is designed around the three fundamental pillars of sustainable development: environmental, social and economic. This sustainable new city is based on innovative concepts that combine urbanization with nature and connectivity, thanks to new digital and AI technologies.

Like the world's major metropolises, Casablanca has embarked on a dynamic process of governance and strategy to better face the new challenges of the century. Since 2016, it has been hosting strategic and academic discussions, illustrated in particular by the organization of the Smart City Africa Casablanca event. After three successful editions, the fourth edition of Smart City Expo Casablanca, was held, on April 17 and 18, 2019, under the High Patronage of His Majesty King Mohammed VI on the theme *"Artificial intelligence at the service of citizens"*. After Dubai, Jakarta and Shanghai in the three previous editions, Bangkok is the guest city of honor. For the organizers of this event, the choice of Bangkok, a city of innovations and technologically advanced in the face of its many urban challenges, could enrich exchanges of experience between the leaders of the Thai capital and the economic metropolis of the Kingdom of Morocco, particularly with regard to problems linked to transport and urban mobility. The 4ème edition of Smart City Expo Casablanca was marked by, among other things, innovation, much-appreciated networking sessions and internationally-renowned speakers. The 5ème edition is scheduled for May 27-28, 2020, on the theme of "*Smart Governance for inclusive city*". However, this edition has been postponed due to the Covid-19 pandemic. A veritable African hub for smart and inclusive cities, Smart City Expo Casablanca has established itself over the years as a must-attend event on the global Smart City calendar. Since its launch, Smart City Expo Casablanca has established itself as a genuine platform for exchange and debate, with representatives from cities, institutions, universities, research centers, experts, opinion leaders and major companies attending to present innovative solutions and projects, and discuss the challenges facing the city of tomorrow. Artificial Intelligence is one of the key elements of future sustainable, inclusive and resilient urban development. Building a Smart city, accelerating digital transformation, urban resilience and territorial sustainability are all enhanced by AI. Questions arise, including: What will the data-driven city look like? What are the opportunities and risks?

Apart from the city of Casablanca, there are other Smart city projects, notably as part of the construction of new towns, among them the flagship megaproject to build the "*Cité Mohammed VI Tanger Tech*", located in the commune of Aouama, in the south of Tangier. His Majesty King Mohammed VI, may God assist Him, presided, on March 20, 2017 at the Marchane Palace in Tangier, over the ceremony to present the megaproject to build the "*Cité Mohammed VI Tanger Tech*" and sign the related memorandum of understanding. The Cité *is a* smart city with a population of 300,000 spread over some 2,000 hectares. The Bank Of Africa Group is investing in this mega-project. The "*Cité Mohammed VI Tanger Tech*" is also the largest Chinese project in the Kingdom of Morocco, part of China's "*Belt and Road*" initiative. This new industrial, ecological, intelligent and international city will be built over a period of 10 years.

The "Fez Smart Factory" project, an innovative Industry 4.0-oriented sustainable industrial zone project, is selected by the Sustainable Industrial Zones Fund (FONZID), following a call for competition launched jointly by the Millennium Challenge Account Morocco/the Millennium Challenge Corporation (MCC) and the Ministry of Industry, Investment, Trade and the Green and Digital Economy. A grant agreement was signed in May 2020. The project is being developed by the Université EuroMed de Fès (UEMF), in consortium with the Confédération générale des entreprises du Maroc Fès-Taza, Alten Delivery Center Maroc and the Fès-Meknès Regional Council. The project area is dedicated to smart and sustainable factories; it will also include a gas pedal for Industry 4.0-oriented startups, as well as a 4.0 model factory. The "Fez Smart Factory" project will be implemented in three complementary phases, the first of which will be completed and put into operation by the end of the first quarter of 2022.

Digitalization is the lifeblood of Morocco's modern airports and ports. These infrastructures use new information and communication technologies and AI technologies, not least to enhance security.

Managers of the Kingdom of Morocco's major ports, notably Tanger Med, are looking to use digital technology to make their traffic more fluid and thus more competitive. They are working to facilitate the entry of ships and speed up their unloading, thanks to digitalization. In addition, more and more shipping lines are using IT technologies to equip their container ships. This technology transforms containers into intelligent, connected objects, enabling them to be prepared for their arrival in port. Connected containers offer enhanced traceability for agri-food transport, cold chains and the transport of live fish. Artificial Intelligence, Big Data and other technological solutions enable ports to be more intelligent in managing a flow, a situation or a customer. Major ports are seeking to capture and anticipate information in order to make the best decisions, improve processes and make them more efficient or cleaner. This competitiveness is sought on both the sea and land sides, i.e. to ensure the smooth flow of goods in and out of the port and during ship-change operations.

On March 29, 2019, the National Ports Agency (ANP) and PortNet SA launched the 1ère edition of Smart Port Days in Agadir, on the theme "*Optimizing export processes at the Port of Agadir*". The aim of this edition is to respond to the challenge facing the port sector, which is to move to a new level of development by focusing more on "*soft*" actions, evaluating port processes and taking advantage of new technological means and the digital revolution. The organizers chose Agadir to consolidate the position of its port, while improving port processes. The 2ème Smart Port Days edition on the theme "*Innovation in the port sector, a voluntary and inclusive approach*" was held on December 11, 2019 at Jorf Lasfar.

During the current crisis caused by the coronavirus (Covid-19) pandemic, OCP Group teams have adapted processes in ports where phosphate products are exported (Jorf Lasfar, etc.) to ensure that ships dock without any contact with crew members. Drones and remote equipment control tools are also deployed. All this has enabled OCP Group customers to be delivered on time.

To support its major strategic projects, the Kingdom of Morocco has positioned the logistics sector at the heart of its economy. The national logistics strategy was launched in 2010 to create a real structural development dynamic for the sector, notably through the establishment of a national network of logistics zones and sectoral action plans. Logistics players are making increasing use of new information and communication technologies and AI technologies, in particular to optimize logistics flows and enhance security.

In November 2018, French telecoms operator Orange chose the city of Casablanca as the location for its structure dedicated to Cyberdefense in Africa. It hopes to make it a hub and center of expertise. CaptureDoc, set up in July 2020 in Morocco, is Kofax Total Agility's exclusive representative in Morocco and French-speaking Africa. It offers a range of intelligent automation services: multi-channel cognitive capture, robotic process automation, electronic document management, electronic signature, intelligent printing, etc. The Realme 6 and C3 smartphone brands have been introducing their "Tech Trendy AIoT" to Morocco since May 2015.

The massive influx of holidaymakers to coastal areas has multiple impacts on health, among other things. But in summer 2020, the inhabitants of these areas can rest assured that they won't be overrun by an army of tourists, since the supply will be greatly reduced due to the Covid-19 pandemic. Nevertheless, to further reassure them and protect health and prevent the spread of the outbreak of the new coronavirus (Covid-19), it is necessary to take adequate measures thanks to AI and robotic technologies. It's worth noting that in Belgium, the coastal municipalities have drawn up a plan ahead of the vacations to keep the expected influx of tourists to the coast in summer 2020 under control. A network of smart cameras will monitor the influx on the seawall and in town centers. The cameras are equipped with software that counts the number of people in different areas and produces a map showing the number of visitors. Belgian coastal municipalities have thus been able to better anticipate and manage the flow of people in the context of the fight against the coronavirus.

Private security, an integral part of the lives of more and more individuals and businesses, has become a growth niche for large and small companies that have specialized in it. More and more of these private property and personal security companies, set up in medium-sized and large companies, are starting to use AI and robotic technologies, including intelligent video surveillance. Several types of connected surveillance cameras are being used. Video surveillance technology is evolving rapidly. In the (rare) intelligent home, a person can easily control the cameras in his or her home from a smartphone, access live video and manage motion detection.

Digital security applications rely on AI systems to automate threat detection and incident response, increasingly in real time. In recent months, due to the Covid-19 pandemic, with teleworking, the figures for cybercriminal attacks on personal, corporate and organizational computers have risen dramatically. This has been observed by specialists in the field of cybercrime during this period of unprecedented health crisis linked to the new coronavirus pandemic.

Artificial Intelligence and robotics technologies are being used in certain environments to combat the new coronavirus pandemic (Covid-19). The health crisis linked to this pandemic has greatly accelerated the digital shift in Morocco. Technological progress has been made in several socio-economic sectors (health, public services/e-gov, education, training, etc.), with the aim of providing users with new solutions that meet their expectations. Artificial Intelligence and robotics technologies are being used in certain environments to combat the new coronavirus pandemic (Covid-19). These technologies include the 100% Moroccan intensive care and resuscitation ventilator, and the Moroccan Intelligent Mask for Automatic Remote Sensing (Midad). In an interview with MAP in September

2020, the director of the Agence de développement du digital (ADD) said that the number of administrations subscribing to the *"bureau d'ordre digital"* and *"parapheur électronique"* platforms had risen from 30 to almost 900 in the space of six months. There is also a *"Télé-rendez-vous"* service.

According to a press release published in September 2020, Valyans Consulting and AIOX Labs have just created AkumanIA in Morocco, a joint venture specialized in Artificial Intelligence and Big Data. This joint venture benefits from the know-how of AIOX Labs, which has been working since its creation to converge international standards in AI and Big Data with the specific needs of Moroccan companies. As a result, Moroccan companies looking for Artificial Intelligence technologies to boost their performance are well served. In addition to Morocco, this joint venture aims to address the entire African market.

The deployment of Artificial Intelligence is still in its infancy in the Kingdom of Morocco. Applications focus only on certain aspects of Artificial Intelligence. The AI market is so interwoven with a multitude of sectors that it is difficult to define its boundaries. It is still in its early stages of development. The main obstacles to the widespread adoption of AI and robotic technologies, particularly in companies, include a lack of skills, insufficient financial resources and insufficient awareness.

In the Kingdom of Morocco, more and more players, think tanks and institutions have recently taken up the challenges of AI.

The deployment of AI and robotics technologies in Morocco is still very timid, particularly in companies and public administrations. They have not yet made the leap to Artificial Intelligence. The use of AI technologies is in its infancy in physical infrastructure and data security, business process automation, adoption of virtual assistants and chatbots, business process optimization, e-Health, e-Government, free-access AI-based e-Education, farmland irrigation, sensor data analysis and IoT.

The market for Artificial Intelligence and robotics is potentially vast. Artificial Intelligence and robotics technologies represent a major opportunity for the Kingdom of Morocco.

f) **Practical use of Artificial Intelligence and robotics applications in the national public security system**

On the domestic front, the Kingdom of Morocco is facing an increasingly complex security situation. Over the past two decades, the Kingdom of Morocco has faced new security challenges and risks.

His Majesty King Mohammed VI, may God assist Him, launched, on January 25, 2016 at the Casablanca-Anfa prefecture, the project to develop an intelligent and optimized urban video surveillance system, thanks to fiber optics and AI technologies. This pilot project, the first of its kind in the Kingdom of Morocco, is being implemented to ensure the safety of people and property, reduce the crime rate, regulate transport flows, automatically detect incidents (driving the wrong way, illegal parking, etc.), identify stolen cars, mobilize law enforcement in good time, and protect public buildings and facilities and their surroundings. The project is jointly financed by the Ministry of the Interior and the Municipality of Casablanca. The plan is to extend this intelligent surveillance system to the most important areas of the city.

A new electronic video surveillance system has recently been introduced in Morocco's major cities. Equipped with fiber optics and sophisticated surveillance cameras for day and night vision, the system can detect and record images and sound of any incident 24 hours a day. These cameras are installed, in particular, at the entrances and exits of major cities, on certain public buildings and in transport stations, airports and ports. They have not yet been installed in certain sensitive areas (soccer stadiums, etc.). The new electronic video surveillance system, which is now being introduced, uses only certain aspects and applications of Artificial Intelligence. Fully functional, practical solutions are not yet fully developed.

As part of the police force's interactivity with citizens, the tracking of videos posted to social networks by citizens, showing criminals, thanks to AI technologies, is still in its infancy.

In some areas, enforcement officers are equipped with sophisticated electronic devices, including surveillance cameras, to detect clandestine activities in areas of unauthorized construction and storage warehouses. These devices have helped to dismantle a number of networks, including the clandestine manufacture of plastic bags. This has enabled the dismantling of mafias operating at night in the Casablanca area (Had Soualem, Sidi Moussa Ben Ali...), among others.

0 The Royal Gendarmerie began using drones for road surveillance in February 2020. It is using drones to monitor freeways in a "*pilot phase*". The Gendarmerie Royale is looking to step up its monitoring of traffic offences, especially those that escape conventional radars. Meanwhile, during the Covid-19 pandemic, in the wake of China, drones appeared in several Moroccan cities, where public authorities use them to broadcast warning

messages, detect suspicious movements in the streets or flush out illegal gatherings on house terraces.

In the Kingdom of Morocco, the practical use of Artificial Intelligence and robotics applications in the national public security sector, in particular to suppress all attacks on people and private and public property, and to rigorously and efficiently combat all forms of crime, is in its infancy.

g) **Summary and conclusion, and general recommendations for tackling the diverse challenges posed by the full range of insecurity situations and sustainable development through Artificial Intelligence and robotics.**

In the era of the digital revolution, in the Kingdom of Morocco, the scourge of traditional illiteracy and semi-illiteracy has been joined by that of digital illiteracy. Public policies, and in particular the e-Government strategy, ignore those who are "*left behind by technology*".

Training in Artificial Intelligence is very recent. In the field of AI, the Kingdom of Morocco, which has attained a threshold effect in terms of digital technology, is still lagging far behind in talent training. Robotics training is still underdeveloped. A solid digital and technological culture is essential for social, economic and political participation. To cooperate with increasingly intelligent machines, workers from all walks of life, from higher education graduates to construction and agricultural workers, will need to acquire new skills. Education and training will have to meet the need to upgrade skills and retrain people. It is up to political decision-makers to define this vast transformation to ensure that no one is left behind.

Scientific and technological research in AI and robotics is in its infancy. It suffers from many dysfunctions.

The Kingdom of Morocco is beginning to develop scientific and technological cooperation in AI with foreign partners, particularly European countries and China. It is necessary for the Kingdom of Morocco to work with its partners to continually advance their strategic cooperative relationships in AI to the mutual benefit of all parties, and to encourage as many scientists as possible to engage in joint research projects.

Digital technology plays an increasingly central role in all aspects of people's lives. But the use of Artificial Intelligence and robotic technologies is still limited. Business demand for Artificial Intelligence is still too low, yet it can improve the operational, logistical or quality management performance of all SMEs. On the other hand, AI is not yet fully put to use in the public sector; yet AI-based solutions can help to effectively and efficiently improve public services in a variety of ways. Their usefulness can be particularly evident in citizens' interactions with public authorities, since they can contribute to the delivery of improved public services.

Artificial Intelligence and robotic technologies raise serious concerns about their responsible and ethical development.

When it comes to national security, the Kingdom of Morocco must rise to the challenges and prepare for the dangers ahead.

Artificial Intelligence is becoming a major challenge for the Moroccan economy, public institutions and human society. It can help pave the way for new possibilities of sustainable, inclusive and resilient development, and help build the knowledge society.

Artificial Intelligence has enormous potential for the common good and for promoting the achievement of the Sustainable Development

Goals set by the international community in areas such as education, health, transport, agriculture and sustainable cities, if AI is developed in a way that benefits the entire nation, respects global norms and standards, and is rooted in sustainable, inclusive and resilient development. AI must be democratized and infused into the everyday lives of people, who must enter the new era with eyes wide open, without sacrificing their values.

The management of public affairs is a prime field for Artificial Intelligence, particularly for making decisions, including politically sensitive ones. Artificial Intelligence has the potential to extend the capabilities of civil servants and public institutions, empowering everyone to do more. To promote sustainable, inclusive and resilient urban development, and make cities safer and more secure for people, one of the challenges of smart cities is to really listen to its citizens, organizations and businesses. Artificial Intelligence can contribute to this, by providing communities with conversational agents who take over from public agents.

Artificial Intelligence has a vital role to play in countering the many threats to global national security and shared prosperity. It holds tremendous potential for the national public security system, particularly in preventing, stopping and punishing acts and activities that endanger national security. It can offer opportunities to strengthen intelligent national security and stability in the Kingdom of Morocco, and to advance sustainable, inclusive and resilient development for human progress.

Mastery of science and technology, in particular Artificial Intelligence and robotics, is an essential complement to technological sovereignty.

AI and robotic technologies are necessary to protect national security and sovereignty, and the development interests of the Kingdom of Morocco. This blessed country must build the levers anchored on Artificial Intelligence and robotics technologies to build its technological sovereignty, security and defense.

With the advent of the intelligent transition, public administrations, businesses and organizations are about to undergo a major transformation. The necessary move towards intelligent transition calls for optimized risk management. We need to develop best practices in Artificial Intelligence and ethics. AI technologies must not only be transparent, secure, inclusive and respectful, they must also guarantee the highest level of privacy protection.

Artificial Intelligence brings with it a great wave of opportunities, provided we're prepared for it. It will shape the future in every field. We need to manage this great process of change in a controlled way. Failure to prepare would be disastrous.

Implementation of recommendations deserving immediate attention to the Kingdom of Morocco to ensure its smart national security for shared prosperity, including comprehensive human security in daily life, strengthen its political stability and promote sustainable, inclusive, smart and resilient development

0 In order to promote sustainable and inclusive growth and development, aimed at leaving no one behind, in a Kingdom of Morocco that is prosperous for all, it is imperative to i) fight against the digital divide, ii) invest in the mastery of technologies by people excluded from the information society to "*leave no one behind*", iii) promote scientific research and innovation, iv) use Artificial Intelligence and robotic technologies, v) promote their ecosystem, in stages, in the field of national security.

a) Need to adapt the education and training system to provide the skills required for the digital economy, including skilled workers with the adaptability and creativity needed to "*work with machines*" and develop a thriving economy based on digital transformation and the knowledge economy

The digital age brings many incredible benefits to Moroccan society, but it also brings many challenges, such as the growing digital divide, cyberthreats and online human rights violations.

Marginalization is growing in the face of the digital divide. There are two levels to this divide. The first-level divide characterizes the divide between those who have access to technology (the Have) and those who don't (the Have Not). It often reflects a social and territorial divide. Many factors contribute to the emergence of inequalities in digital access in Morocco (age, level of education, economic situation, socio-professional category, geographical location of place of residence or work, etc.). The gaps between urban and rural areas of residence in terms of technologies, and in particular ICTs, remain glaring. The second-level divide is the lack of digital skills. As a result, many people are excluded from the digital society. The digital divide has become an issue for human society. Indeed, the use of ICT is now intimately linked to the notion of employability and productivity. Among other things, ICTs can help prolong professional activity by improving working conditions (teleworking, adaptation of tools), improve quality of life and combat social isolation. They are also likely to play a role in access to public services, participation (in the literal sense), mobilization and networked communication.

Given that many citizens are deprived of the skills and competencies essential to the digital age and the achievement of the Sustainable Development Goals, building a human information society in Morocco for all, based on inclusion, requires tackling the factors blocking the use of ICTs, taking into account the diversity of uses and creating the conditions of technological and scientific culture that remain prerequisites for the absolute development of all new knowledge. This requires, among other things, the strengthening of digital capabilities, which must be more needs-based and adapted to individual circumstances. Bridging the digital divide requires digital literacy, which is the process of equipping a population with ICT concepts and methods, and putting them in a position to perform the usage practices that will enable them to appropriate these technologies (and first and foremost the use of the computer in a networked context). In addition, taking charge of people excluded from the digital society requires computer equipment and the commitment and training of trainers.

b) Intelligent use of new technologies

New technologies, especially the digital technologies underpinning the main functions and infrastructures of human society, need to be put to optimum use. The intelligent use of new technologies requires continuous learning to enhance the capabilities of their use, and extra effort to make the most of the opportunities they offer and meet the challenges they pose.

c) Creating an environment conducive to unleashing the prodigious potential of Artificial Intelligence technologies to enhance overall national security and improve citizens' living conditions, by stepping up investment in science, technology, engineering and mathematics education, key drivers of the AI development ecosystem.

At present, true participation in the digital age requires, among other things, the acquisition of the necessary skills, including learning by learning to play better and better, keeping up with Artificial Intelligence and robotic technologies, including understanding, reasoning and interacting differently with AI, and a high-speed connection to the Internet.

d) Intensify efforts to train the cutting-edge AI skills Morocco needs to take advantage of the AI revolution, and stimulate the creation of highly dynamic startups developing AI-related use cases.

The growing need for solutions based on Artificial Intelligence technologies highlights the need to train more highly qualified experts and top-level researchers in the scientific fields underlying these technologies (mathematics, computer science, data science...). It is necessary to organize training for diversified talent pools, to adopt a holistic approach to science and technology, by integrating science and technology into the education system, to invest in trans-disciplinary education and the creation of new knowledge, to design research and technology support programs with an AI component, and to organize training (in number and content) for Artificial Intelligence-related technological professions, and to stimulate the creation of start-ups specialized in Artificial

Intelligence, by creating a favorable environment for their emergence and development.

.

e) Promoting scientific and technological research on AI and robotics, including fundamental research, to develop new products or services in Artificial Intelligence, stimulating innovation in trustworthy AI, ahead of technological developments and respectful of fundamental rights and ethical rules, making the most of the opportunities offered by AI and robotics, and meeting the challenges they pose and the challenges facing the Kingdom of Morocco: considerable national security issues.

Artificial Intelligence and robotics are multi-disciplinary fields of scientific research with a bright future. AI applications concern all human activities. Understanding the differences between machine and human learning mechanisms is a major focus of AI research. At the same time, the need to design AI applications to strengthen national security is crucial. It is imperative to promote Moroccan research in key scientific and technological fields for AI (mathematics, computer science, data science, social sciences...), and to increase human ingenuity in a responsible way.

f) Strengthening and diversifying sources of funding and direct investment for science, AI and robotics technologies and innovations that enhance national security and facilitate the achievement of sustainable development goals for human progress

To support scientific research and innovation in Artificial Intelligence and robotics, particularly in academia, public authorities need to strengthen and diversify sources of funding and direct investment in these fields. The government must take steps to mobilize resources from all possible sources of funding, including public-private partnerships, especially given the financial constraints arising from the current economic crisis. It must take action to support Artificial Intelligence in R&D and the experimental development of innovative digital services, notably through research and innovation tax credits and subsidy programs.

g) Promoting the use of AI and robotic technologies in national security in all its dimensions, the ecological crisis and the promotion of sustainable and inclusive, intelligent development and shared prosperity

The feeling of insecurity is at the crossroads of real insecurity and subjective insecurity linked to factors such as the erosion of social ties, job insecurity and urban planning. People living below the poverty line are insecure. Insecurity is an inequality. As a fundamental good and an essential factor in quality of life, security should be guaranteed to each and every one of us. It is essential to a healthy economy, to collective and individual development, and to social and territorial cohesion. It is a daily concern for elected representatives, company and organization managers, but also for all citizens, who should become active players. Artificial Intelligence technologies can help to combat the factors of fragility that generate insecurity, particularly that linked to crime, which is made up of objective insecurity (all acts of delinquency) and subjective insecurity (the product of feelings of disintegration of the social and urban fabric, increasingly precarious living conditions, etc.).

h) The need to put the transformative power of AI at the service of the Moroccan economy, organizations and citizens for a better and more prosperous future for all, a future ensuring human control, trust, security, stability, promotion of economic opportunities and environmental sustainability.

AI technology is a key area for promoting economic diversification and transformation, productivity and competitiveness. This new technological revolution directly concerns all players in Moroccan society. We need to make this new technology both a driving force for our economy and a vector for social progress, and to promote the dynamism of Moroccan entrepreneurship in the field of AI, by creating the conditions for the development of the Artificial Intelligence industry.

i) Promotion of Artificial Intelligence, a disruptive solution for monitoring and exploiting information to effectively and efficiently improve the Kingdom's economic security, a cardinal component of the nation's security, ensuring that the economic crisis does not become a security crisis.

Artificial Intelligence is a guarantee of economic security, a major guarantee of strategic autonomy.

j) Fighting tax evasion and avoidance with AI to strengthen the sustainability of public finances and financial stability.

Artificial Intelligence is a formidable weapon in the fight against tax fraud and evasion: an Artificial Intelligence tool capable of comparing millions of data sets to track down tax evaders.

k) AI, the linchpin of Business Intelligence at the service of the Kingdom

The term "business intelligence" is constantly evolving in terms of form, definition and application. Broadly speaking, business intelligence is concerned above all with information, through its collection, transformation and dissemination, as well as its use by and for decision-makers.

There's a link between Artificial Intelligence and Business Intelligence. Thanks to its potential applications and contributions, AI is put at the service of Business Intelligence. The use of AI is a powerful asset in a game of economic warfare.

l) Widespread adoption of explainable, transparent and responsible Artificial Intelligence in all sectors of the Moroccan economy

The use of digitization, in particular Artificial Intelligence, robotics and connected objects, is transforming companies involved in the production of goods and market services. This will have a positive impact on the business climate, guaranteeing total transparency and fluidity for optimal service to citizens and investors. AI technology brings with it socio-economic changes that we need to prepare for (training, adaptation of professions, etc.). The popularization of Artificial Intelligence promises significant quantitative and qualitative advances in the economy, but at the same time raises fundamental societal questions (national technological sovereignty, ethics of choice, distribution of wealth and remuneration of work).

m)   AI applications in the field of public health safety (risk assessment...), a strategic component of the nation's security, serving, among other things, emergency situations, to advance health for the good of all: offering a myriad of tools thanks to digital and artificial intelligence technologies

Artificial Intelligence applications are helping to improve the quality of care, among other things. AI is indeed at the heart of the medicine of the future, with assisted operations, remote patient monitoring, intelligent prostheses, personalized treatments thanks to the cross-referencing of a growing number of data (Big Data), etc.

n) Artificial intelligence for smart cities and regional planning, with a view to job creation, economic prosperity and sustainable, inclusive and resilient development.

The digital transformation of territories and the use of Artificial Intelligence are a major asset for promoting the competitiveness and sustainability of national territories. They open up boundless prospects, whether in everyday life (simplified administrative procedures), healthcare (tele-medicine) or education (connected universities). AI and robotics technologies are at the heart of the use of technological innovations to improve quality of life, ease traffic congestion and preserve the environment. They provide innovative solutions that enable cities to become healthier, safer, cleaner - in short, more pleasant to live in. For example, the development of smart power grids makes it possible to adjust the flow of electricity between suppliers and consumers. We need to build smart, connected, efficient and inclusive cities, which will improve citizens' quality of life, be more competitive and attractive, and represent a new way of approaching the urban fact, with a view to meeting the growing challenges linked to habitability, accessibility, sustainability, urbanization, socialization, citizenship and metropolization. AI technology is one of the key elements in the future development of the rational territory.

o) Artificial Intelligence revolution to help prevent and manage natural disasters

Advances in Artificial Intelligence benefit the prevention and management of natural hazards, particularly floods and flash floods. Today, mixed reality technologies will help prevent and manage environmental risks. Mixed reality enables a person to interact physically in a real environment with virtual elements in three dimensions, using a dedicated headset. With a view to adapting to climate change, frequent flash floods need to be better anticipated and managed. Artificial Intelligence applications are needed to predict the evolution of events and facilitate decision-making.

p) AI, a challenge for the future of public services to combat the factors and impacts of insecurity, among other things.

The State, local authorities and other public and semi-public institutions must fully seize the potential of AI. By freeing civil servants from certain tasks, AI could enable them to refocus on their core business, for better service to users. The use of digital technology and Artificial Intelligence is a lever for the global transformation of human society and public action, with a particular focus on the development of digital services for citizens.

q) Artificial Intelligence, a guarantee of better living for citizens

Digital innovations play a crucial role in economic, social and cultural sectors, particularly those linked to the quality of daily life of Moroccans. Artificial Intelligence technology is currently shaping a groundswell that will fundamentally transform the individual, human society and the economy. It has immense potential in terms of, among other things, social good. It will play an essential role in everyday life. It has the potential to extend human capabilities, giving everyone the means to do more. Today, AI is a civilizational challenge, and a guarantee of a better life for all our fellow citizens. It needs to be democratized and infused into everyday life. We need to contribute to its understanding and apprehension, for all and by all.

r) Artificial Intelligence for national defense and homeland protection

National defense is at the heart of the issues raised by the development of Artificial Intelligence. Artificial Intelligence appears to be the best way of perfecting the tools used to defend and protect the homeland. In these areas, artificial intelligence is making solutions possible.

Artificial Intelligence is becoming increasingly strategic for national defense and homeland protection, as it effectively and efficiently facilitates logistical and military operations, including remote operations via robots; it enables the development of sophisticated tools and equipment, including a new generation of fighter aircraft capable of countering the advances of intelligent air defenses; and it lies at the heart of tomorrow's combat technologies.

s) The need to guarantee a high level of cybersecurity

Artificial Intelligence is strategic, as it lies at the heart of cybersecurity issues. Cyber attacks are becoming increasingly sophisticated. With the acceleration of digital transformation, in an environment subject to growing cybersecurity imperatives, the need for detection and protection is very strong.

t) The importance of AI for national security and sovereignty

Moroccan mastery of AI technologies (and not just their use) is a matter of national sovereignty and security. The Kingdom of Morocco needs to grasp the major challenges of tomorrow, anticipate and exploit the potential for scientific, social and economic progress offered by Artificial Intelligence.

u) Using the National Population Register and the Single Social Register in AI applications for security and development

Research Group calls for access to Single Social Register data to carry out its mission

v) True impacts of AI on human society, the economy and public institutions, including the real potentials (socio-economic, cultural, human...) of smart national security using AI and robotics for a better and more sustainable future for all

In implementing its project, the Research Group is committed to assessing all the true impacts of AI on human society, the economy and public institutions. The social, economic, cultural and political impact of Artificial Intelligence technologies could be significant, as they could be used in all segments of human activity. The Group is responsible for proposing actions in its respective fields (research priorities, technology transfer, sectoral impacts, ethical and socio-economic consequences, etc.) to promote the optimal integration of Artificial Intelligence into Moroccan human society.

w)   The need to ensure an appropriate ethical and legal framework for AI and robotics research to secure a better future and foster shared prosperity

AI and robotic technologies must not only be transparent, secure, inclusive and respectful, they must also guarantee the highest level of privacy protection.

x) Now is the time to take action to promote the Artificial Intelligence and Robotics ecosystem in order to, among other things, promote intelligent national security for shared prosperity, including comprehensive human security in everyday life, strengthen stability and promote the sustainable, inclusive, intelligent and resilient development of the Kingdom of Morocco.

The Kingdom of Morocco must assert its ambition to be a European leader in artificial intelligence, and turn this leadership into a factor of attractiveness by making its companies more competitive. This objective must guide the actions of public authorities and economic players alike: the aim is to enable France to be known and recognized as one of the most advanced countries in artificial intelligence, offering the best conditions for its development. France's leadership in this field is an important factor not only in attracting foreign talent, but also in keeping the talent trained here in France. France should be the obvious choice for anyone with a passion for artificial intelligence, whether they're a researcher, investor or company founder.

It is necessary to: i) create the ethical, human-centered and trustworthy National Safety Commission on Artificial Intelligence, with, among other things, a structure for assessing the impact of algorithms, and an ethical committee for AI technologies, ii) create interdisciplinary centers bringing together, among others, philosophers, historians, sociologists, engineers, biologists, physicists and computer scientists to confront their ideas and reflect collectively on the impact of technologies on Moroccan human society, iii) ensure competitiveness and shape the conditions for its development and use, iv) to create a legislative and regulatory environment conducive to the advent of AI that can be relied on without fear, v) to put in place formal accountability mechanisms, including in the public sector, particularly in the exercise of regalian functions such as security or law enforcement, vi) draw up a national strategy for scientific and technological research and the development of the Moroccan AI ecosystem, to accelerate the transition between research, particularly academic research financed by the State, and applications (administrative, security, economic and military....) by facilitating the appropriation of AI technologies by institutions and the economic fabric, ensuring preparation for the future through training and research, developing an ecosystem potentially conducive to the emergence of genuine "artificial intelligence champions", strengthening national sovereignty, integrating AI into key global national security missions, stimulating innovation, economic growth and well-being through AI, and promoting sustainable development.

IV) The need for a structure to lead the strategic AI technology research project.

Artificial Intelligence and robotic technologies are strategic technologies with a prosperous future; they involve social, economic, cultural and political interests, as well as national security. It is necessary to better understand the foundations of these technologies, to better assess the scope of these technologies' solutions, to properly identify the organizational changes that Artificial Intelligence implies within an organization, and to properly align Artificial Intelligence with the systems already in place within an organization. The time has come for public deliberation. The time has come for intelligent strategic action, to steer the economy towards innovation and high-quality, technology-driven growth, including that linked to Artificial Intelligence and robotics, to develop a strategy in which all stakeholders play a role in advancing a safer and fairer Digital Morocco, which will lead to a better and more prosperous future for all, and to give direction to AI technologies in order to maximize benefits and limit unintended consequences and misuse.

a) Given that Artificial Intelligence has become a strategic tool for many States around the world, and that it is a technology of the future, involving the Kingdom of Morocco's economic interests, national security and technological sovereignty in the field of Artificial Intelligence, it is necessary to set up a State structure responsible for carrying out the aforementioned strategic project.

i) to create this structure, given the crucial importance of its missions requiring the use of strategic and confidential information in Artificial Intelligence algorithms, at His Majesty's or at the Ministry in charge of National Defense Administration

ii) to name this structure Centre/Institut national de recherches pluridisciplinaires en Intelligence Artificielle et robotique or Centre/Institut Royal de recherches pluridisciplinaires en Intelligence Artificielle et robotique, a center of excellence promoting innovative AI in the service of intelligent homeland security, responsible and human-centered, in line with human rights, fundamental freedoms and shared democratic values.

Bibliographic list

1. Alan Turing, Jean-Yves Girard, The Turing Machine, 1995 , Computers and Intelligence, pp. 133-174

2. Claire Rémy, Artificial Intelligence, 1994

3. Jean-Marc Alliot and Thomas Schiex, Intelligence

4. artificielle et informatique théorique, CEPADUES, 2002

5. Michael R. Genesereth and Nils J. Nilsson, Logical Foundations of Artificial Intelligence, 1987

6. Stuart Jonathan Russell and Peter Norvig, Artificial Intelligence, Pearson education, 2006

7. Quand le robot va en classe à ta place Sciences et avenir - 01 juillet 2017 - n°845 - pp.94-97 Lecomte, Erwan

8. Les Robots humanoïdes entrent en scène Sciences et avenir - 01 février 2017 - n°840 - pp.88-91 Hertel, Olivie

9. Les Machines autonomes par-delà le bien et le mal La Recherche - 01 juillet 2018 - n°537-538 - pp.97-100 Ganascia, Jean-Gabriel.

10. J. Ellul, La technique ou l'enjeu du siècle: Economica, 1990.

11. Ass. Pénombre, Chiffres en folie -Petit abécédaire de l ' usage des nombres dans le débat public et les médias: La Découverte, 1999.

12. D. Bourcier, P. Hasset and C. Roquilly (eds.), Droit et intelligence artificielle

- A revolution in legal knowledge: Romillat, coll. Droit et technologies, 2000.

13. A. Desrosières, La politique des grands nombres - Histoire de la raison statistique: La Découverte, 2010.

14. E. Morozov, Pour tout résoudre, cliquez ici - L' aberration du solutionnisme technologique : Editions FYO éd., 2014.

15. D. Cardon, A quoi rêvent les algorithmes - Nos vies à l'heure des big data: Seuil, coll. La République des idées, 2015.

16. N. Colin, H. Verdier, L' âge de la multitude - Entreprendre et gouverner après la révolution numérique: Armand Colin, 2015.

17. A. Supiot, La gouvernance par les nombres - Cours au Collège de France (2012-2014): Fayard, coll. Poids et mesures du monde, 2015.

18. J. Markoff, Machines of Loving Grace - The Quest for Common Ground between Humans and Robots: Harper Collins Publishers, 2015.

19. S. Abiteboul, G. Dowek, Le temps des algorithmes: Éditions Le Pommier, 2017.

20. P. Jensen, Why society cannot be put into equations: Seuil, 2018.

21. R. Durand, L'évangélisme technologique - De la révolte hippie au capitalisme high-tech de la Silicon Valley: FYP ed. 2018.

22. A. Garapon, J. Lassègue, Justice digitale - révolution

graphique et rupture anthropologique: PUF, 2018.

23.   A. Basdevant, J-P. Mignard, L ' empire des données, Essai sur la société, les algorithmes et la loi: Don Quichotte, 2018.

24.   P. Janot, Lex Humanoid, robots and judges: Editions Thot, 2018.

25.   E. Sadin, L ' intelligence artificielle ou l ' enjeu du siècle: Ed. L ' Echappée, 2018.

26.   J.-G. Ganascia, *L' I ntelligence artificielle: vers une domination programmée?* Le Cavalier bleu, 2017

27. S.   Russell and P . Norvig, *Intelligence artificielle* , Pearson, 3rd ed. 2010

28. A. TURING, "Intelligent Machinery, National Physical Laboratory Report", in B. Meltzer and D. Michie eds, *Machine Intelligence* , vol. 5, Edinburgh University Press, 1969; "Computing machinery and intelligence", in *Mind* , vol. 59, no. 236, pp. 433-460, 1950.

Milton Keynes UK
Ingram Content Group UK Ltd.
UKHW021035190124
436321UK00001BA/99